THE LIES WITHIN
A SHATTERED CURRICULUM
By
David W. Redkey

Published by TBI Writer, LLC

D1253828

Published by
TBI Writer, LLC

Copyright © 2021 by TBI Writer, LLC.

ISBN: 978-1-7377893-0-7

Dedicated to my family.

I do this to make you proud.

Acknowledgement

I would like to thank my wife Aggie who designed the cover of this book, helped edit the manuscript, and gave creative feedback. Without her assistance, I know I would have never finished this book. Her strength silenced my self-doubt and insecurity. I love you from the bottom of my heart.

For my children, my love for you is why this book came to fruition. I hope you are proud of me for speaking out and sharing what millions of people experience every year. I want this to be an example you live by and strive to achieve as you get older. Also, remember that whenever someone says you can't do something, I want you to prove them wrong with a smile on your face.

Preface

This work stems from my own experience before, during, and after my time in the Arizona Teachers Academy. So, I can state how the vast majority of everything mentioned in this book is 100% true. A few things were added for dramatic purposes, events condensed and switched around for dramatic effect, and some interactions were fleshed out to get to the heart of the problem. Everything else is golden. Sadly, I am cursed with crystalline memory. So, I share my experience as a story because I believe the truth will win in the end.

As a certified teacher, my view of the profession was spoiled by the actions of the real people on which these characters are based. Even though I change the name and genders of many of the characters in this book from their real counterparts (and in some cases making their actions more overt), I hope the people in question receive a wake-up call to become better people. Life is too short to be so vile to others, especially against people who are just trying to become a teacher and make the world better.

Because of a long history of school administrators and teachers misbehaving, I hope my story about a school district allegedly covering up transgressions by their own employees and those related is seen as the truth. I am above resorting to sensationalism. This is simply a reminder of how power can corrupt a person or a group of people who are flailing wildly to maintain their grasp on any authority they are given.

~David Redkey

INTRODUCTION

August 5th, 2020

Even though I graduated from the Arizona Teachers Academy in December of 2019, a semester late because I received an Incomplete on my student teaching assignment as retaliation for asking to be moved out of an abusive union member's classroom, I am still unable to get a job as a teacher — contrary to all of the statements about Arizona needing teachers. I was promised a teacher's contract would be waiting for me when I was done with the program, but the only thing I can find is working as a substitute teacher without benefits and with shit pay. By shit pay, I mean substitute teachers receive about $100 a day (a maximum of $18,000 per year) and no benefits compared to a teacher in Arizona averaging about $320 per day with benefits.

Because substitute teaching does not count towards my one-year of service to fulfill my Arizona Teachers Academy scholarship, I will be forced to pay back the $20,000 as well. I will be slapped with a $20,000+ unsubsidized student loan, and I will be forced to make payments starting next year.

I think a lot of this has to do with me speaking up about some union members who happened to be teachers at *The School District* where I was student teaching last year. Regardless of me being placed at one of the biggest Union-backed school district in Arizona, I didn't let my voice stay quiet while they did what I would consider illegal activities. I spoke up and now I am blacklisted. I took a stand because I couldn't allow a few public-school-teacher-equivalent-of-carpetbaggers push me around and try to belittle me.

With me seeing lines and lines of teacher candidates at every teacher fair, I now believe that this "teacher shortage" is just lip-service so the Union teachers can get more money from Arizona families, get paid a lot better than other professions that have to work almost 52-weeks a year.

Even with all the fucking email communications between me and people from *The University* and *The School District*, the Civil Rights Division of the Equal Employment Opportunity Commission told me I have no case. *The School District* is perfectly able to treat me differently as long as they don't say my traumatic brain injury is a basis for their denial to hire me, interview me, or provide me any chance of becoming a teacher.

The U.S. Department of Education? Nope. *The District* is legally allowed to conspire to prevent employment of a teacher who speaks out, speaks up. *The University* and *The School District* are legally allowed to disseminate my protected educational information as long as the information relates to anything related to education. It does not matter if the information is false.

The Arizona Attorney General's Civil Rights Division? Nothing. They basically supported the same view points of the U.S. Department of Education and the EEOC.

The National Labor Relations Board? HAHA! The NLRB said they do not regulate State employees. This falls under the purview of some unnamed governmental agency. I was never told who, and I was ghosted when I asked.

So, I will write in this journal, looking over all of the emails that were exchanged, so I will remember. I saved all my performance evaluations from my TK20 account (the program teacher candidates have to pay for so their performance evaluations can be saved and scored) and all of the email communications to and from people at *The School District* and *The University*, and the negative actions that occurred after I brought up my concerns of being mistreated (Pro-Tip: if an organization wants to tell you information over the phone instead of sending an

2

email, they are likely trying to keep information unrecorded). It isn't going to matter in the long run, but I like to know the muck that spews forth from some of the educators.

Even with a large number of fantastic educators in Arizona, I know there are enough spoiled apples to ruin the whole bushel.

~Sam

January 2nd, 2018

On a cool and sunny day, drastically different from the blaring heat of a typical Arizona summer, I am sitting in the living room of our white house, a house at the start of a cul-de-sac where the civilization gives way and wilderness, nature, and the beginning of a large mountain takes hold. To further increase the scenic feelings of the area, a vast nature preserve exists behind our house as well. It's very nice. It's very comforting. It's almost like paradise.

The house was built in 1996. Surprisingly, my house's textbook location shows the developers knew where to manufacture track homes allowing families to find a place to relax. I bought this house because the collapsing housing market allowed me to get this on the cheap, and I grew tired of paying the mortgage and property taxes of others.

Prior to buying the bank-owned property, part of me was deeply hurt because I knew one of the previous owners was likely disabled (the grab bar in the master toilet was a giveaway). So, I couldn't let this go to investors looking to flip this lovely house into a rental property.

After washing away all thoughts about how I found this house on the cheap, my focus turns to the present. I look at my partner, my love, and I feel a sense of discontent with my current job. The only employment that will hire me; even after earning two college degrees, a Bachelor of Arts in English and a Bachelor of Arts in Communication; is the same type of soul-sucking customer service jobs I did for 12 years before I finally attending college. Because I did not take up internships while I working towards my degrees at *The University* (thinking my number of credit hours will help me easily find a new job), I settle for working as a customer service representative for facilities cleaning and maintenance company, allowing me to get a steady paycheck but lacking job security.

But enough is enough!

I decide it is time to make a change.

Deciding enough is enough of being trapped in the same type of dead-end job that goes to people with less education than myself, I open the computer, transition to a news website, and see a story — front and center — about a program designed to combat the teacher shortage in Arizona.

The Arizona Teachers Academy was founded to help combat the ballooning class sizes and teachers leaving the profession in record numbers by removing one of the pitfalls of being a teacher (student loan debt). Even though Governor Ducey and the Republican Party has received considerable flack for their policies regarding education, I believe his program aligns with my sincere desire to be an educator.

Because the program allows students to become teachers without taking on enormous student loan debt, maybe I can undo the mistake I made when I transitioned out of *The University's* education program after transferring from my community college to finish out my degree in 2014.

Since I now possess two bachelor's degrees I earned in 2016 and a 4.0 GPA, the Arizona Teachers Academy advertises how it will offer to pay for my master's degree in education and setting me up to work in the field I originally attended when I started the education program at *The Community College* in 2013. The promise of a fully-funded teacher's certification program and job waiting for me upon graduation is almost too good to be true. This is my chance to right the wrong I did to myself. I would have already been an educator, but I was just led astray by actions of his predecessor Governor Jan Brewer.

Part of me is glad the Arizona Teachers Academy was established. Arizona hemorrhaged so many educators. So many classes were being left unfilled by a trained teacher. I finally get the chance to undo the mistake I made in August of 2014. I should easily find whatever position at whatever school I desire when I am done. I will happily join the legion of teachers educating the youth of Arizona, walking along the side of many others who give students the truth, provide them opportunities to gain wisdom, and shepherd them towards being citizens who will add to instead of take away from our society.

Although the grant requires matching years of teaching to offset the number of years of funding, my singular focus is being the best educator possible for the rest of my working life. The students deserve it. Arizona deserves it. I will do my very best.

When I look back and remember all of the happiness my teachers shared with me and my fellow classmates, I tell myself how I was born for this profession, even if my history is not as happy as others. Where I came from will not matter. What I survived to have this choice will slip away into background noise. I feel in my very bones how teaching is a lifelong career, not a simple avocation. I know a pension will be waiting for me when I eventually retire. I will also have a load of memories of all the students I guide towards a productive life, many of whom can and will be better able to positively shape their own communities.

With this significant life commitment, my journal represents a chance to write down my thoughts and experiences as I transition from my pointless, mundane job to educational conductor, writing symphonies with each and every student that takes my class. I will also connect each entry to moments in my past to help remind myself of how far I have come and why I will continue to fight for the good of us all.

Fortunately for me, my two college degrees and my prior two years of training to be a teacher while attending community college will give me a leg up on others who enter the program fresh without ever stepping a foot in the classroom as an adult. I am salivating at how my prior college experience allows me to fast track towards getting a state-funded master's degree by the summer of next year.

I'll fill out the form to enter the graduate program, pay the graduate application fee, and the funding from the State will be mine. Now, I know the grant will save me from spending over $20,000 just to make a teacher's salary. Currently, my two bachelor's degrees are only netting me low-paying jobs, barely above minimum wage; so, this is gonna be a large pay increase when I am done.

Even with the amount of money I will see come my way as a teacher, I don't wish nor desire placing myself into another enormous financial hole by taking over a year to get a graduate degree without having a job. So, I will just suck it up, and I won't miss my one shot to find the career I've been dreaming of.

So, I will make a change, a drastic upheaval of everything I hold dear, not some insignificant deviation from the norm requiring self-deception to sleep well at night. Oh, those sweet little lies I tell myself to conform to a lifestyle robbing me of meaning, stripping away my humanity until nothing is left than this withered husks whose future is being alone in an old folks' home, fading away to nothing. I will not allow this, permit this to be my future, my fate.

When I worked for the CDC-INFO line, I would teach the public general health information as a form of assistance, locate facilities in their area where they can seek medical attention, and even communicate with state officials about concerns regarding various diseases or even potential health events. Even though all of this was done before I returned to school (with only a high school diploma), I still felt like I was doing a world of good helping the public. Now, with my level of education and years spent in college and university, I feel like my current *job* working as a customer service representative documenting maintenance requests for banks on the east coast was not my dream nor my goal when I left CDC-INFO to go back to school. This is not helpful to future generations. I only continue to move the wheels of industry, making sure our technicians fix the minor inconveniences plaguing a company whose only drive is to house and manage the money of others. When a person doesn't have enough money in their account, the bank will rob those people even more, putting them further and further back into a hole, making nearly impossible for them ever to be whole again.

By working within the customer service realm, by knowingly being in a position that helps the business maintain the façade of assisting the community, the numbing dissatisfaction festers, spreads, ripping away my hopes, my dreams, my soul, my reason for continuing on in this painful existence. Now, I know I am just another cog, but my side hurts too damn much to delay, to avoid changing my fate. The pain, emotional and physical, originates too deeply beneath the surface for me to do nothing. My scar tissue surrounding my once broken ribs, broken by a driver who took a red lights to signify merely a suggestion, represents my beacon for change.

I grip my side every few minutes, massage away the discomfort from scar tissue starving once-broken ribs of vital oxygen to repair, recuperate. The pain radiates whenever I move around, walk around. A constant reminder of what I survived and how I am unlikely to enjoy what will account for nothing but a short-lived life.

Even though I could stop focusing on the banality of my existence, the self-pity has an intoxicating aroma that I cannot help but inhale with giant gulps. Depressing thoughts form in my mind: *Has this walking, talking piece of meat reached its zenith? Or was survival a false opportunity to escape the perpetual nadir and ascend to new heights?*

STOP IT!
STOP FEELING SORRY FOR MYSELF!

I push away the pain with new vigor. I will make a difference. Why? I want to be a teacher, an educator. No! I need to be a shaper of young minds. I have been told by educators how the job is a demanding profession, but the doctors said the same thing about me when I had feeding tubes nourish me and machines helping me breathe. My doubters must've thought I'm not made of sterner stuff. They did not know what I survived nor how precarious the terrain I traversed really was. Words are cheap when the person knows nothing of your history. How many people lie in a mangled piece of human engineering, unconsciously gasping while attempting to breathe, the kind of gasp where a bystander will say, "He's alive?!"

This has happened to how many? Millions? Thousands? Hundreds? Ten? Or maybe just one? Can we really say what I survived is the usual course of events?

I digress. I am too sanctimonious. I should count myself lucky because when I was sitting in the lunchroom at the rehabilitation center three months after my accident, seeing people who could not even talk, and I would honestly switch my place with them because it may be easier than being conscious of my own limitations or the limitations that society places on people like me. This chip on my shoulder is the one who survived when everyone else said I would just be a mindless, hopeless drooling lump of proteins, fats, water, and shattered dreams.

So, I will be an educator. As an educator, as a difference-maker, I will be the explainer of what *this is* or *what that is* for minds yearning to be filled. I guide them, give them a chance to shape their own destiny. All I need to do is move them towards their own promised land. In curing them of their ignorance, we hope they will leave the world in a better place than we left it. We strive to add a brightness to their days (or at the very least a silver lining on their dark, dark clouds).

I get on my computer, and I navigate towards the education program section on *The University's* website. In addition to the typed-in application with the standard graduate program fee, I need to upload my passing score for the English Language Arts NT301 Arizona Educator Proficiency Assessment (AEPA) test and also upload a video resume, allowing me to be judged not only on my written word but also on the way I convey myself over curated video.

Considering a Master in Secondary Education costs over $20,000, I think it is an excellent opportunity to save a little money, especially if I can find a position at one of the more lucrative schools. There is an advertised teacher shortage after all; so, I shouldn't have any difficulty finding a job after I am done — something that pays more than the $30,000 working as a Customer Service Representative.

What should I say?

What could really encapsulate ethos, logos, pathos, and kairos? I know they ask us to shape our speeches to answer why someone like me would deserve the money. So, I just need to answer how I could take my skills and adapt them to help students in need. Should I plan my speech or speak from the heart?

I begin to ad-lib my speech like a normal round of competing in impromptu or extemporaneous speaking at a high school speech and debate tournament or a collegiate forensic tournament.

I try.
I fail.
I try.
I fail.

Each subsequent performance gets closer to the truth but always feels a bit far off. I initially tried improving my speech, repeating the same words while making quick modifications on the fly, but I was never satisfied with the end result. I always stumbled, interjecting a few *umms, uhhs,* or just a bit of awkward silence. It took me about seven takes to realize that every word needs to be written down, planned, and provided the same level of care and control given to my own performances when I was at a speech and debate competition. Preparation shows the audience you care about them. Considering I am striving to be a teacher, and apparently teachers need to spend a lot of time preparing for class, I need to show the committee for the teacher's scholarship that I possess the same care and patience with my own application as I would if I were teaching a class a typical school. So, I write down my speech, channeling what I felt could open me up to an opportunity to reach up and grab that money out of their grubby hands. I am transcribing my speech for posterity's sake, so those words do not fade away to nothing.

"For my submission, I am going to focus on an obstacle I actually had to overcome to attend college.

"In January of 2007, I was in a car accident. I suffered multiple right rib fractures that caused respiratory failure, and I also had a lacerated liver. The medical staff stated the injuries caused agonal respiration. Additionally, I had a subarachnoid hemorrhage, a left frontal lobe hemorrhagic contusion, and a grade II diffuse axonal injury primarily in the corpus callosum. Those traumatic brain injuries should have ended my story right there. Even though doctors informed my family that I would be in a lower state of consciousness if I ever woke up from the coma, I proved them wrong. This speech, me being here today, is a testament to my undeniable will.

11

"When I returned to work, I was dissatisfied with it because I had so many different skills that I was not utilizing. So, I decided I needed to return to school.

"Even with some of the lingering long-term effects like my impulsivity, I enrolled in my local community college, became a member of Amnesty International, and joined the Forensics Team — where I won awards for Program Oral Interpretation, otherwise known as POI.

"Once I graduated from the community college, I transferred to your University to join the interdisciplinary college. I eventually wound up getting a Bachelor of Arts in Communication and a Bachelor of Arts in English.

"With the completion of those two degrees right there, my accomplishments signified that when a barrier reared its ugly head, a roadblock likely stopping many people, I not only overcame those inconveniences, but I also thrived.

"As a person un-ironically born on the Labor Day holiday, I will labor continuously to improve the education of students, meaning you would make a grave mistake by not allowing me to become a member of your teachers' preparation program.

"Thank you so much for your time."

As I finished the words, turning off the camera, I knew this covered everything I needed to say in the most concise message possible. I believe this is an excellent video resume. My background and what I worked through, coupled with the written resume that details my college degrees and awards I've won, likely means I will be accepted into the program. All of the accolades guides my hand towards seizing and pulling into reality what only exists as vapors. My chance to finally become someone that will make my unborn child proud of my accomplishments, brought about by my own perseverance, will no longer elude me.

Memory before the Arizona Teachers Academy

I shouldn't just be flippant about my experiences or why I decided to enter the teaching profession. As I stated before, I need to go into more detail about my motivation. The sum of my experiences led me to decide on taking up a career in education. So, a connection to any and all events from my past, my childhood, will remind me, when looking back, of why I strive to teach students.

All of this started with something simple.

Mom, a very kind woman who gave birth to me when she was 21-years-old. Even though she was very protective of me and my sibling, even though she would be described as "big-boned," she was a meek and gentle woman who loved both of her children unconditionally.

Despite her loving nature, she also had a side that aligned less to what constitutes an ideal parental caretaker. All of it was based on an illness that medication couldn't control. When the prescription drugs could not help her, when the depression and anxiety would take hold, she would hoard food for reasons unknown to my brother and me. She even told us that she would forget that she went to the store and the urge to shop overwhelmed her.

During a particularly debilitating episode, my family lived at an apartment complex off of Townley Ave and 7th Street. The money my Mom spent because of her mental condition caused a drastic change to our lives. The disease caused her to blow through her monthly disability money, leaving us without enough money to pay rent or utilities.

Dad was angry. Really angry. He didn't say or do anything violent or aggressive towards the family, but the sheer disappointment and fear of what our future would hold were clearly visible upon his sunburnt face. When it came to us, he would always express anger with obscenities. Regardless of how he conveyed his anger,

13

sharing his worry about where we will live in the next few days, we were still faced with the possibility of being forced to live on the street.

In hindsight, what were my sibling and supposed to do to stop our mom from going on a shopping spree? My mom was a grown woman, and Taylor and I were in third grade (I was held back in kindergarten due to absenteeism). How could my sibling and I help a mom who went into one of her episodes and forgot how much she spent, how much money she wasted by going to the store repeatedly while my father was at work? How could we have helped her? Could we have even stopped her? Unfortunately for all of us, my 10-year old and my sibling's nine-year old selves were powerless to deviate our course.

When my Dad came home after a long day doing landscaping at someplace in Scottsdale, he saw all the packages of food in the kitchen. The refrigerator was stocked, but there were even more formerly frozen, thawing items sitting on the countertops, leaking water as the cool of preservation slowly melted away — forming puddles on the kitchen floor. Besides being absolutely livid, my Dad quickly inquired about what happened.

When he finally figured out where all of this food came from, how my mom acquired so much, he realized we were in serious trouble. He knew we couldn't afford to live there any longer; so, we needed to hurry up and find a new place to live before the manager came snooping around asking for the exact time when the rent would be paid.

With even saving up all his wages and not buying any more food for the rest of the month, we would not have made it before eviction papers would have been drawn up. We were as good as gone, so my Dad started asking around for places we could stay. He wasn't comfortable having us move to a homeless shelter because he didn't want anything to happen to Taylor and me. He also didn't want Mom to be placed into a position where she would be raped again (one of our neighbors raped my mom a few months after we moved to Arizona).

I guess with my Dad asking around, he found a place for us to move to on short notice. So, my family and I were required to leave in the middle of the night without saying goodbye to our friends. Taylor and I were even forced to leave behind a bunch of our toys for the resident apartment vultures to sift through once we were gone.

So, the little panacea for our momentary problem was to move into a hotel off of 36th Street and Van Buren. The utilities were part of the package, and we could go down to the office every morning for a bagel and coffee. But, in the early 90s, it was less than an ideal place to live.

Unfortunately, in the early 90s, children running around and unattended were less than the epitome of good parenting, especially if the children were only in the third grade. Additionally, our temporary neighborhood suffered from vicious, cyclic poverty, a plethora of drug dealers, prostitution, and any and all crime, including murder. Keep in mind, this was before any attempt of the State wanted to clean up and improve the area as a way to attract new out-of-state businesses or bring in local development. So, my family and I were stuck in what I would call my nadir.

Also, once we were trapped in the nexus of living in short-term rentals, my family quickly learned how challenging it became for us to find a more reputable place to live in a less crime-ridden area. Once we had the eviction on our record, no one wanted to give my parents the time of day. So, we were stuck living out of hotels.

The real problem of living out of hotels was how prices were charged based on season, meaning we were forced into hotel-hopping the entire time we lived in that part of town. To help offset some of the seasonal increase in prices — likely playing a role in us not moving as much or being completely homeless during those chaotic times, my Dad would contribute as a handyman for some of the locations. Even then, his work was only a temporary reprieve. We would still need to find a new place to live every couple of months.

During the entire time my family lived on Van Buren, we lived at the East Phoenix Motel, Jackson-Smith Lodge, and Jamison Mills Short-Term Rentals near the old site of Bill Johnson's Big Apple (now closed) and the 37th Street and Van Buren Pete's Fish and Chips (also now closed).

As a short break between staying in the hotels along Van Buren, we also lived in a furnished apartment hotel off Scottsdale Road. It was near Old Town Scottsdale, and we were almost within walking distance to The Sugar Bowl, but we only stayed in the Scottsdale area from late spring to early winter, covering the end of my fifth grade and the start of sixth grade. We then had to move back down to Van Buren for a couple of months before Mom's caseworker found us an apartment in the Sunnyslope area.

Either way, the hotel-hopping living situation introduced a new sense of isolation due to the total lack of any children our own age around us. I guess that was a reason why Taylor and I made quick friends with a slightly younger kid.

What was her name…?

Sally?

Yeah, her name was Sally. She lived in a condemned, collapsed house, a house that looked like it was struck by a bomb, and everything was collapsed except the roof. She attended a Thomas J. Pappas school — a school for children who lived on the streets, and she was sometimes picked up in front of one of our hotels where we stayed. Anyway, Sally was pretty cool, even though she enjoyed roaming the streets.

Whether true or not, there was always an air of danger roaming the streets when we would go out alone, but since my sibling and I always stayed together (and

Sally sometimes tagged along), it was never really a problem. It also didn't hurt that we were poor. We could have been incredibly fortunate not to die at this young age or being human trafficked to some other location and never seeing our parents again. Part of me felt that our poverty cast a safety net where people didn't even bother with us because we were dirty, malnourished children.

But even if poverty did provide some protection, we never took the chance. By remaining together, I think we staved off being the victims of some unseemly event. For example, the time Taylor, Sally, and I walked all the way down to this out-of-the-way convenience store to play some arcade game. That would have been a perfect opportunity for all three of us to be taken away, but I guess three of us would have been too much for a bad guy to overpower and control. At least one of us would had a chance to get away and notify an authority figure, if they cared about people like us. Of course, it doesn't hurt that all three of us could run really fast when the time required.

A typical day was like this, my mom was usually at home asleep because of her medication, or she was watching daytime TV. When he was not doing handyman stuff for wherever we lived, my Dad was out in Scottsdale or Paradise Valley doing landscaping. So, we had the freedom to do whatever we wanted when we wanted.

In a way, what we did would have been likely frowned upon by society, but we did not concern ourselves with whatever would be considered proper conduct. We were just children. We wanted to find enjoyment to distract all of us from where we lived, how we lived, and more than likely the pain from our empty bellies.

Our favorite pastime was always playing the Street Fighter II Championship Edition arcade machine at the Circle K off 35th Street and Van Buren. We would sometimes go to another convenience store closer to 28th Street and play King of Fighters. Every so often, we would change it up by walking over to the arcade at Tower Plaza, but that would take what felt like hours to get over there. Regardless of where we played games, the memory of all of us huddled together in front of the arcade machine is one that I truly cherish. Nothing like *the winner stay in, next player up*. I remember those moments so fondly, so vividly. If only I was better with names. The passage of time has allowed those memories to become honey-sweet to belie the reality of my childhood and how my life could have been so much worse or even a whole lot shorter.

January 3rd, 2018

    I am so excited for my application, dreaming when I can guide students into building themselves up. As their teacher, I firmly believe each and every pupil under my care will steamroll through any barrier in their way, making this world a better, more thoughtful, more understanding planet.

    In a way, my students will be my legacy. In a way, I will vicariously improve the world through their actions. In a way, I will continue to live on, way beyond when my injury catches up to me, leaving me as only an emptiness in the form of a survivor who breathes, blinks, appears alive, but is nothing but a void beneath the surface.

    Either way, I am beyond nervous. Will they accept me? Will I have problems if I tell my future students about my past injury? I never remembered any of my teachers ever surviving or talking about a brain injury. If any of them ever did, I guess they kept it to themselves. But if I am the only one, why not be the first one who breaks the barrier? It has to start somewhere, right? Why would a school district have a problem with someone like myself, considering they serve students who identify as disabled all the time? If anything, it may offer the students in need a chance to build a better connection to education and to me as a teacher, allowing my job to be much easier overall while improving their relationship with the public school system.

    I mean, if someone overcomes a problem, a problem that would give the person a chance to just stay at home collecting disability for the rest of their lives, and they decide to return to the workforce in general and the public education field in particular to make a difference, why not allow them to assist future generations? Wouldn't that be someone worth looking up to during these turbulent times post-Great Recession? Wouldn't that be someone who would be a model of what we can achieve, even in the face of adversity, when we set our minds to it?

I believe in a society that values people regardless of their upbringing and/or any potential disability. A school should be the perfect place to put that thought into action. The mighty public school is a community of people from many walks of life, many histories, and many different ability levels. Now, this may be romanticizing public school system, but I still honestly believe anyone willing to work with children who faced a horrible upbringing or submersion beneath the dark waters of an atrocious home life will be more than willing to accept a co-worker like myself. After all, the news constantly goes on about a teacher shortage, so this is the perfect opportunity to undo the mistake of leaving the program, even if they are hesitant to hire someone like me. I believe the shortage may cause the administration to look past a teacher in the classroom who has a survived a traumatic brain injury and support the needs of students for a qualified educator who survived a tragic backstory.

But the more I think about it, the more I see darkness spread from the human condition, becoming even more depressed while I patiently wait to receive my rejection letter, wallowing in self-pity. I might get rejected because it will be so easy to find a reason disregarding a potential employee, labeling them as unfit. After all, my health condition may make students uncomfortable (or whatever asinine excuse that suits their agenda). People like me are replaceable since there are so many uninjured candidates looking for jobs. They will instantly view me as less than or unable to perform because someone like me *obviously* suffers from limitations.

I will prove them wrong.

Not too long ago, I dragged myself up from the rocky dirt, wiping away the grit and small stones piercing my skin. I even looked the physical therapist in the eye, not with contempt, but with pure determination to not let this be the bookend of my story. My look said, "I will journey much farther than this injury." I had no choice in deciding what happened to me, but I will sure as hell be the one to determine how this story ends. I am the only one who writes my pages. Everyone else is just players guiding me, helping me, or hindering me — and all other combinations in between.

On a brighter note, my life partner taught me a delicious recipe. It is nothing more than a combination of mixing a unique concoction of umami, garlic powder, all-purpose spice, salt, hot pepper paste, ham, and cheese into my ramen pot. Still, it is so delicious and so satisfying. But the whole entrée kind of defeats the purpose of me attempting to watch my carbs, but it tastes *oh so good.*

Also, the fact that a soup is mostly water, allowing a greater intake of the beneficial fluid, a must when we live in such a hot and arid city, should offset any negative repercussions from consuming my partner's special recipe. But what are my alternatives? Considering fast food has all of those chemicals and garbage in it, I guess this will be better for me by default. The worst thing that can truly happen is the deprivation of some instant gratification and chemical reward from the consumption of junk food, even though the afterglow is filled with nothing but regret.

For a person who has a damaged brain, I should watch what I eat to prevent further injury because of high blood pressure. After all, I want to be old enough to see my youngest child go to their wedding — if they decide to get married.

I know society dictates that my partner and I should love our children unconditionally, no matter their choices. Still, I also can feel the pressure of the collective whole forcing us to conform to the prescription of how I dictate my children's development into whatever type of mold that likely contributes to the production of future offspring. But I shouldn't worry myself about what they will do now or in the future. Instead, I should just worry if I provide the best example of an adult to them, an adult they can emulate and be proud of following, copying, or even creating their own mold to pass on to future generations.

Oh, the worries of being a parent. The constant push of making sure they are safe but while also worrying if they will also grow into the best possible versions of themselves in the process. I guess I can only do what any other parent does and just hope for the best.

Memory before the Arizona Teachers Academy

My family was ALWAYS broke. Considering my Dad's minimum wage employment and my mother's reliance on Social Security Disability Income due to her inability to work because of medical reasons, it kind of makes sense our constant shuffle from one hotel to the next during those tumultuous years. People with more money could afford living out of much nicer houses, especially houses that didn't have live mice running in the walls. They could afford luxuries like a cable television to watch TV all day, a stove that will make soup piping hot, or a shower that isn't stained with God knows what.

Sally, our kindred spirit and who was always an expert at avoiding her friends when she was not in the mood to hang out with us, was the friend to who we related the best to out of everyone else we knew. Her home life may be different, but she was the closest to us when it came to living through the proverbial wreckage of the American Dream. For a kid that lived near our school David Crockett Elementary, she was extremely challenging to find. I guess it made sense when thinking about it logically. It is kind of hard to locate a kid who possibly lives out of a collapsed, condemned house.

Considering she called such a dilapidated structure home, I should have understood how she successfully avoided being tracked down by Taylor and me. I believed Sally followed the strict rule of *you'll find me when I want you to find me.*

Taylor and I would often walk down 37th Street to attend David Crockett Elementary School, a part of the Balsz Elementary School District. We would always travel next to the empty undeveloped desert lot with overgrown bushes, walking on the sand ledges bordering the field, feeling cool as we walked almost level with houses of the surrounding neighborhood. Near the back of the school, there was a hole in the fence. Through the hole, we could enter the school and walk through an playground that hadn't seen children for the day.

Every time we walked this way, my sibling and I would see Sally's destroyed house, and we would peek to see if we could find her anywhere. With all the times we walked the well-trodden path to school, she was never to be found. We would even call out to her but to no avail. Maybe she didn't feel like hanging around her house that much because it was basically destroyed (the lack of running water and electricity would also explain why she was never there). Another, more sensible reason would be she might have been tired of us.

I guess it might have been the latter because that one time we were playing some fighting game at this out-of-way convenience store. We tasked Sally and her skill of gaining money from strangers to help fuel our quarter-crunching play. We always saw her do it whenever she wanted something; so, I guess it may have been her last straw with us.

Looking back, I shouldn't be surprised Taylor and I burned that bridge by leveraging her skills begging for money to extend an enjoyable afternoon for Taylor and me. Or, we didn't actually know how she actually got her money when we were not around and all the trauma tied to it. It may have been something that neither my sibling nor I could have ever imagined (or even been cool with). We were only third graders. Taylor and I were likely privileged not to be forced into doing something unspeakable to gain a little cash.

We could have always panhandled ourselves without burning that bridge? Right? Pride was the only thing keeping us from being equals. In our situation, we should have learned a better way to navigate getting what we wanted when we needed it.

Getting back on track, we did not have a penny to our name. So, because we didn't have money and were too proud to panhandle, we just asked Sally to do the dirty work for all of us. I ultimately rationalized my inability to beg for money, looking as pitiful as possible, because I was too shy and ashamed, and my sibling just followed suit. But there is also a severe societal vulnerability for asking for money, money that rationally would not be used in the exact way we *always* promised to whoever would give it to us. Also, this vulnerability could make people think our parents did not care about us, or they could decide that we didn't need to be on the street any longer and whisk us away. So, we would shove down any hesitation with the activity by allowing Sally to become an extension of our own need for gratification.

I felt terrible, especially now in hindsight, that we leveraged her skills to have a little bit of mindless fun. We exploited Sally and her natural ability to connect to strangers — strangers with money — as a route for us to gain a few mere moments of electronic escapism from a world of poverty, especially Taylor and me.

In reality, I think she lowered herself to begging for money because she was just looking for friends (humans are social creatures, after all). But, Sally could relate to us based on our shared home insecurity, but we just used her need to play video games.

If games were out of the question, I don't know if she would have wanted to come over to our house. We never invited her over. And the question never came up. I think it never came up because we were never really her friends. But even if we were best friends with Sally, there was a level of discomfort even allowing her to see the circumstances my family was in — a level of control we were not willing to give up.

Even with my inability to really push Sally to come and visit our hotel room to play games, the problems my family-of-four suffered over the course of those three years, living out of studio hotel rooms a few times really harmed any opportunity for her even see how we lived (or the scattered roaches that would disappear when we turned the light on). Ultimately, we never found out if she would have accepted us and our home life. We never gave her that chance to judge us too harshly.

I can forgive myself for this guilt by looking back at the living situation. I think I was too shy and self-conscious to allow her to see where we lived. I think it is likely the same reason we were never really close to someone we claimed as a good friend. It was just smoke, mirrors, lies shrouding the truth we intended to hide from everyone, especially those who we suckered into giving us a little bit of money.

Sally, Taylor, and I were all felt ashamed about the stains of poverty, felt less than even though none of us had any real control over our living situation. Even those who are on the bottom rung of the ladder, scrambling to hold on for dear life, will still feel a level of vulnerability when others see how poorly and mistreated a child is when the veil drops, illusion gone.

The formative time in my development of us living in a trailer was less than ideal, but my family still found a way for it to work. We still had a living room (even though it was way too small for company) where my Dad slept on the couch, a middle office/bedroom where Taylor slept, and then there was the back room with the king bed where Mom and I slept.

When we lived out of the trailer, there was an opportunity for us to have people come over, but no one ever did. I guess being forced to sit on a dirty King-size mattress while playing time-traveling ninja games would be a bridge too far. But if it was during the many times we were staying in a studio hotel room, I believe there would have been no way for us to have any friends over...period.

On the bright side, we had this excellent 24" CRT TV that allowed Taylor and me to huddle close and play whatever video game that we had at the time. Even if the colors were not the most vibrant, and the picture was sometimes fuzzy, I could still be wholly engaged every time a game was turned on.

Considering the situation we were in, I guess this was an effective distraction to keep us from focusing on the drudgery of every day. Part of me misses the simplicity of that poverty. My entire existence, even living in a trailer, was so much easier than now. The years between middle school and graduating high school had an ease to them based on our total lack of anything. However, the sane part of me doesn't miss walking across the street to the liquor store near the Western Lodge to buy single cigarettes for my Dad, buying a Milky Way in the process, and opening the candy bar to see it was all white and filled with maggots. I would give anything to give up that part of my childhood in an instant.

January 4th, 2018

Being forced to wait patiently after paying so much money is eating away my focus. I really want to know if I am worthy. I know my video resume submission played on all four classical rhetorical appeals: *logos*, it would only be logical to accept someone like me as a teacher who has a background in English and Communication; *ethos*, the structure of my presentation, and the suit I was wearing should convey that I am a person of the utmost integrity; *pathos*, how my pitch emotionally resonates with whoever will listen, convincing them I am the right candidate for the scholarship after I survived a traumatic brain injury; and *kairos*, the rhetorical timing of my speech is appropriate because Arizona is in desperate need of teachers, and someone with my educational experience and how I moved beyond the limitations of a brain injury will be an ideal candidate for a profession that is in desperate need of role models.

If the Secondary Education program accepts me, I will try to be an English Teacher. I know it doesn't make a lot of sense because when I was in high school, AP Biology was the only test I received a four on without studying. In comparison, I scored a three on AP US Government, a three on AP US History, a three on AP English Literature, and a two on AP English Language. The AP Lang has always been a sore spot because my high school didn't offer an AP English class for 11th Graders. I didn't care because I was offered an opportunity to take the test for free; so, I had nothing to lose. Either way, I rectified this inequity of my AP Lang score by taking a rhetorical writing class while attending *The University*.

My excitement is overflowing because the knowledge and experience contained within this brain can flow forth and supply my future students with determination and grit, especially students like me who were not dealt a fair hand at birth. They are the students who need the most help, and they tend to be the most overlooked.

Considering the only job I could find after I graduated summa cum laude from *The University* with two bachelor's degrees (earned concurrently) was the same type of dead-end employment that preceded me finally attending college for the first time, I was Sisyphus made flesh. No matter what I accomplished, no matter what designations I earned, no matter what awards I received, I always wound up pushing this infernal boulder up the treacherous mountain without any illusion of release.

My college degrees, though, were the small consolation to the scars left by the roof of my car, a roof that curved up and slammed into my head, marring my flesh, scarring my brain. Therefore, even with the degrees not allowing me an opportunity to really show my skills, the Arizona Teachers Academy would give me the chance to realign my wayward journey towards something superior in every way. Therefore, I will take this opportunity to change my course, establishing a chance to open up young minds to the importance of language.

With a publically-funded graduate-level secondary education program, this will make it so much easier for me to join the vanguard of educators, hoping to build a future and get a pension in the process.

Why couldn't a teacher who grew up in extreme poverty, who grew up with an empty stomach as a regular occurrence, who grew up scrounging for clean clothes to go to school every day — missing school when nothing could be found, who grew up being excited about what treasures we would find whenever we received a food box, who grew up knowing the feeling of being adopted by a charitable organizations for the Christmas holidays, who grew up with dental care being next to nothing, who grew up hanging out constantly at a friend's house with the hope we would be invited for lunch AND dinner, who grew up in a home infested with bedbugs and seeing them flee from an old couch that my family decided to set aflame to get rid of them, who grew up utilizing super long extension cords from the neighbor's house as a way to have electricity, after we paid a nominal fee for such a service so we could have the electricity to watch television or even have lights on to drive away the dark, why can't all of those experiences coalesce into an educator who rose from maggot-filled refuse and become a public school teacher? Why couldn't someone like that represent an ideal model for students struggling to show up every day, many of whom are keenly aware of the difficulty of a child's life and barriers preventing their education during the Great Recession? Someone with such real-life experience as myself would be an ideal candidate to teach. Would I not? What type of person would think otherwise?

I receive a ding in on my phone, telling me that I just received an email. I open my phone, navigate towards the email section, and I see I received a message from *The University*.

I open the message, hopeful.

I am now a member of the Arizona Teachers Academy!

Memory before the Arizona Teachers Academy

Darkness. A deep penetrating gloom envelops me. A void of thought, an emptiness of dreams where everything enters, passes over the event horizon and disappears forever. Within the blackness, what felt like an endless pit, I drown in the uneasiness of dread. Yet, even within the pitch-black, everything was calm.

Still.

No sound.

No movement.

Anywhere.

I couldn't see anything.

I couldn't feel anything.

I couldn't think anything.

But, I knew I was somewhere *wrong*.

Where was I? How did I get here?

I felt around in the darkness. The ground was small, little valleys with round plateaus. With the tops having a smooth roughness and the small valleys having a hard grittiness, my mind pieced together the only logical explanation: a stone floor. I continued to crawl and trace my fingers slowly across the leveled, but at the same time completely unleveled, terrain, moving along every nook. I continue crawling and feeling the floor. My mind is mapping the location, trying to picture what my eyes cannot see, so I may be able to put my feet to work.

My fingers were stopped by a resistance — hard and matching the floor — but this time ascending: stone walls.

I stood up.

Even though my eyes couldn't see anything, my mind was at ease knowing that there was a solidness beneath my feet. I didn't have to fear falling this very second.

I began to slowly move around the stone wall, slowly guiding myself with my left hand, making sure the wall continued, and my left foot was making sure there was a floor to stand upon. If there were lights, it would likely have been a very comical situation for an outside observer. But none the less, I was pressed firmly against the wall, feeling with my left side as I inched along.

I come to the first corner. The joint was held together with the same mortar used to firmly fix the stones within the floor. A rational thought percolated in my mind — *feels like this floor's sole purpose was to keep the walls upright*. This section went straight up as far as I could touch. I didn't know if it reached the ceiling, but it didn't stop when I couldn't reach up any higher.

As I passed the junction, the next wall was the exact same. Same feelings to the touch. Same textured stones. Same sand-like mortar. I don't know what kind of place this was, and I didn't understand why I would trapped be in such darkness, but I did not worry about it as much because I was focused on at least trying to find an exit.

After I passed the next wall joint, I continued my slow and sure movement. I felt along, but my fingers slipped through the solidness into a void. I could not put my whole hand through. But where the tips of my fingers could find true passage, I felt an emptiness, a lack of anything on the other side. The empty space between the bars only allowed four of my fingers to enter at once.

Also, I find that something solid, smooth prevented my whole hand from going all the way through… I figured the solid hard feeling was a metal bar. I slid my hand across the metal bar, slowly, surely. I counted there were only three bars.

I quickly processed all the feelings. I deduced the most logical explanation was probably the most nonsensical. I was in a prison cell, an old-time prison cell.

But why?

I don't know why I was here. I felt like I was being watched by someone or something. The incessant tick in the back of my mind reminded me that I was not be alone, even if I thought I was. But I could not for the life of me remember how I got here.

Alone? Why would I be alone? Did I do something wrong? What could I have done wrong? In what way could I have fallen short so much that I am confined in this darkness?

This bottomless, impenetrable pit was something beyond foreign to me. My mind could not comprehend the limitations, the boundaries, placed before me. This was clearly a punishment that did not match any level of failure. This was an inhumane retribution, a forfeiture of freedom far outweighing any type of crime a person like me would have ever committed.

In all of my years of existence, I was never the type of person to attempt to cause strife in other individuals. I was calm and collected. I was beyond timid to the point where I could not even look another person in the eye. I know I was not a person who would have tried to break the law or go out of my way to harm someone else. So, why was I here? A sneaking suspicion crept over me like I was here for something I didn't do.

I was framed?

No.

That didn't make sense.

My mind circled towards another possibility.

This was a penance I took upon myself because my grandfather did something wrong, and I took the blame. I think he killed someone, but I couldn't be too sure. It was horrific.

Something that couldn't be taken back.

I just wanted to get out, but I had nowhere to go, no one to plead to. I did not deserve to be here. No one did. Regardless, I was stuck here nonetheless. So, I tried to make do with what was available to me, feeling around blindly, hoping to find a way to remove myself from such a horrible situation.

So, why were the lights out? Why wouldn't my captors let me see?

I tried to grab on to something… something… felt… searched… my hand touched a solid object.

Hard.

Cool.

Smooth.

Metal?

I opened my eyes to blinding light, white paint on the walls, and the metal rails along both the left and right sides of whatever I laid on. Around me, I see monitors and a metal cylinder. The blinding light was coming from the fluorescent lighting on the ceiling above me.

Why was I on my back?

The room was white, sterile, and clean.

The light? Little tubes of fluorescent illumination.

It felt weird to breathe. I reach up and touch a hard tube coming out of my throat. I didn't try to pull at it because of fear of what might happen. Instead, I run my hand down, and I touch another tube running from my stomach on the left side.

What the fuck is this?

Where was I?

How did I get here?

The ache and tingle resonating from my right side was an unwelcome discovery. This pain nagged. Never strong enough to register a cry of discomfort, but unpleasant enough to chip away a moment freed from my previous imprisonment. This new, unwelcomed friend. This little nagging pain was my new companion.

I saw a woman. Her mouth was covered with remnants of dried saliva. A purple shirt with the ghosts of food long since consumed stained the front. The shirt was loose-fitting because it was bought second-hand, just like the stained grey sweatpants she was wearing. There were more than a couple flakes of dried skin in her dark brown hair, tinged with streaks of gray (must be dandruff and old age). The possible names associated with this face were slow to unfurl, but after a moment that seemed to carry on forever like a boulder blocking the mountain route through my brain, a deluge of information came rushing back towards me once the mental obstruction was cleared. A proverbial storm surge of information overwhelmed my senses. The clouded memory; so very fragile, so very thin; shattered.

This was Mom.

Was this a bed?

Why was Mom sitting next to this bed-like thing with bars to make sure I didn't roll off?

What was this tube coming out of my throat?

What was coming out of my belly?

Such questions came to my mind, but such trivial questions had to wait for a later opportunity for exploration. There were more pressing matters to be explored, answered.

"You were in a car accident," she whispered to me, with care and concern only a mother could show. I don't know how long she had been sitting here, but I was still wondering when was the last time she had a chance to bathe and cleanse the concern and worry that only parents with children in the hospital would really know. I knew it wasn't her fault. It was the damn disease that kept her from being able to properly care for herself or us. So, even though I was in bed, even though I escaped a prison of my own mind, my heart filled to the brim with sadness.

How long was she here?

I wish I could do more.

Lips that had not moved in what felt like weeks finally sprung to life to form a straightforward phrase. The only statement that would make sense in a moment like this (and such a revelation to accompany the first conscious gaze in how long? Days? Weeks? Months?). Then, finally, the words came together, a symphony of hope that I did not have a patient lying next to me whose injuries were because of my ineptitude: "Whose fault was it?"

Simple.

Direct.

Looking at me, with all of the concern in the world, she sweetly replied, "Oh honey, the other guy ran a red light."

August 16th, 2018

After my acceptance to the program and finishing my summer course work, I am starting my Fall Internship while also completing six evening and afternoon courses across both sessions. Three of the courses are during Session A (August 16th-September 30th) and the other three are during Session B (October 10th-November 25th). This is to get the major academic grunt work for the degree out of the way before the main course of the Spring Semester.

The entire point of the internship is to just have the teacher candidate travel to a school once a week, work with the classroom teacher, who is designated as the intern mentor teacher, and get a quick preview of what teaching will be like. With Fall Session A and Fall Session B, the four-month internship counts as a full two-semesters of interning in a school under a normal, non-accelerated program. Once the fall internship is completed, the teacher candidate will move to another school for student teaching during the Spring Semester of the current academic year.

With student interning in the fall, student teaching is in the Spring Semester, and Summer Session A counts for the last few credits on the degree path (the master's degree can be picked up the following week after the final grades have been posted). So, I should be done with the entire program by June 27th of next year, especially if I finish the Arizona Educator Proficiency Assessments (AEPA) Professional Knowledge Examination a few weeks before completing the program. Then, with the Letter of Completion from *The University* as proof of me fulfilling all the training requirements to be a teacher, my passing test scores on both of the English Subject Matter and Secondary Education Professional Knowledge

Examinations, and my freshly-minted Master of Education degree, I can take all the information down to the Arizona Department of Education to be awarded a standard teacher certification — not a provisional teacher certificate given to a teacher candidate who only has a bachelor's degree. In addition, the Provisional Teaching Certificate is valid for only three years, whereas the Standard Teaching Certificate that comes with having a master's degree lasts six years.

For my internship, I was placed in Phoenix School District (PSD) and at Larry Itliong High School (LIHS), meaning I need to travel about 32 miles — roundtrip — for my required in-class training. I asked if I could go somewhere closer, but the program denied my request. They basically told me they would put me anywhere, in any school that will accept someone like me, and that would be that. I even brought up that I could intern at a much closer location where Ms. Lilly Artez, one of my former classmates in the teacher preparation program during my time at community college, was a teacher of the same subject as me (English). She would have helped me gain real expertise while also allowing me the opportunity to help out someone I admired as an educator.

Sadly for me, the program would not allow me to work with her because they didn't want someone to give me an unfair advantage. I am a little upset about the decision to deny me an opportunity to intern with a colleague who went through the same community college education program as me; moreover, her school would have been a 15-mile round trip, meaning I was more likely to be a member of the community that her school served, increasing the possibility of actually working there when I finally receive my certification from the State in July.

So, the program just ships me over to LIHS.

Even though I am heartbroken by the news, I realize that getting more experience in a different community will allow me to bring in fresher perspectives to the classroom when I get my chance to work for Ms. Artez's high school in next fall. Also, only coming in one day a week was not much of a hassle anyway.

After spending about six hours helping and observing my intern-mentor teacher, I will have to travel 20 miles to *The University* for evening classes. Nothing like checking off some boxes to make sure I receive a proper state-paid education.

It still kind of sucks that I travel all of this way to the school just to come in for a single full day, once a week, but I guess this is to ease me into taking over a class next semester. With my mentor teacher teaching his class, I can see how a professional easily guides his students. Furthermore, with the help of my new mentor teacher in the spring, I should have a full slate of tools to start my new job at the end of July, making an extremely smooth transition into managing five periods of about 30 students each around 150 eager total.

Even though I really hope to make a difference with future generations, I view the once-weekly commute a total drain since I have to drive almost an hour to get to the school site from my house (and it is about the same distance to my college). I honestly thinking *The University* nor *The School District* are taking into account the amount of money I will need to spend just to continue this activity.

Still, I should have guessed the teachers' program would have placed me at such a far-away location as LIHS because maybe they figure I get a lot handed to me because of my injury. So, instead of Mountain Top High School, where Ms. Artez teaches her English classes. They want me to go all the way out to the middle of nowhere, waste a ton of money on gas, and just observe. There is making something hard, and then there is making some very hard.

Anyway, my first impression is the entire school has about six single-level buildings for traditional classroom work. The gymnasium, near the track and football field, towers over all the other buildings except the massive auditorium near the front of the school. This means the entire school is all spread out, providing the students an opportunity to get a lot of steps in. Also, I guess it is a way to make them healthier overall since childhood obesity is a real public health concern.

When it comes to the classrooms, *The School District* tries jamming as many students in as possible, with desks crammed together, allowing maximum funding per room. With Arizona, all of the school districts receive about $14,000 per student from the State. So, if Mr. Mark Cichy, my mentor teacher the internship, has about 150 twelfth-grade students, the school should receive about $2.1 million in 18-19 funding for the five groups of students Mr. Cichy teaches in 2019 alone.

With crammed classrooms, and if the 12th Grades have six classes each, the teachers for all six class periods would account for approximately 14.2% of the school's total State and Federal Funding for teaching students. The remaining $1.8 million-plus for the Class of 2019 would be spread around for other items to help promote the best learning environment available for the students, allowing the school to excel academically (if money buys excellent student performance). So, cramming students into classrooms does not just equal more money; it is also good business sense.

Either way, I hope this is not my classroom when I get my own class next year. I honestly feel the number of students is too fucking much. I never experienced anything like this when I was at my old high school. Still, I guess that also could come from me taking all Advanced Classes. Also, my school had an evident socioeconomic divide because it was on the outskirts of the Central Corridor, an area along Central Avenue in Phoenix where a lot of wealth has accumulated due to its significance to the Phoenix economy because of its centralized location and the city was basically developed on a grid-system.

Because of this and many students from that area preferring my high school instead of their assigned school, cliques quickly formed. Some came from wealth, or the illusion of wealth, while others could be labeled as mind-numbingly poor (like yours truly). So, I guess the students at this school are herded along, letting the State pay their way, and subsequently jettison when they age out of public school funding, resulting in many students not finishing high school.

So, I can understand why public schools want students with money attached to them in the building because their wealth may benefit all of the other students. But, I can also see why schools do not want money to follow the students because that would negatively affect the high-paying positions within the school that depend on enrollment to bring in the tax dollars allowing such jobs to be funded in the first place.

Oh, I almost forgot!

Mr. Cichy did not decide on being a teacher when he left high school. The six-foot-one, reasonably trim, blond-haired, and blue-eyed educator originally wanted to be a lawyer, but employment did not work out for reasons he would never share; so, he fell into the education field. Mr. Cichy, known to his students as Mr. Cinch, the nickname the students would call him to his face, was given to him because of his prompt attitude on getting students to turn in assignments.

My mentor teacher moved out here because the teacher employment market was extremely competitive back Eastern States. He couldn't find a job outside of substituting.

So, he moved out here to sunny Phoenix, Arizona to get a teaching job. Fortunately for him, he also found a fringe benefit and quick employment by starting a relationship with someone at the district office, bringing a whole new meaning to the idea of how it is not WHAT you know, but WHO you know, something that holds true even for teachers.

That is exceptionally insulting, especially for a person who spent two years earning my associate's degree at a community college focusing on my secondary education, then transferring up to receive my two bachelor degrees, paid tens of thousands of dollars to learn the ins-and-outs of English, entered a graduate program to become an English teacher, to only see how little the school actually values the foundational subject form of discourse in the majority of social settings in the United States. I watch my hope dissipate when realizing how little politicians and administrators care about the qualifications of who they have teaching the most spoken language in the United States. This is akin to how traffic laws are something we value, but we rarely follow or even care about as we run through red lights with reckless abandon.

Feeling a deep and profound sadness is the only response I can muster when thinking about how little the school system cares about teaching students the ability to even read. Even the finer details, details that will separate low-level writers from the upper stratosphere of literacy was almost absent from the Mr. Cinch's classroom. Teaching English correctly appears to be lost in the realm of the Arizona curriculum, or at least in Mr. Cinch's classroom.

He always likes blaming the lack of literacy within his classroom on the earlier grades. "They are the ones who should teach students how to read, how to write," he would often say to me.

For example, Mr. Cinch, who supposedly was a master of his field at the school did not even know the difference between prescriptive and descriptive language. This person, with his limit understanding of the very language he is paid to teach, is supposed to guide me into how he teaches the subject to a classroom of 12th Graders. The crème de la crème is how he doesn't even understand that language is an arbitrary social construct.

For example, there is nothing "orange" about the word "orange." There is no orange-ness about the word. The word is nothing more than the subjective utterance that society agrees should be the English designation for the wildly popular citrus fruit.

By giving students this framework, I don't know, maybe the students will understand better that what is said and how it is depends on the circumstances. Either way, I really hope he covers that later in the semester. If anything, I can give him a few pointers because I believe it will really help his students, especially the students who are English Language Learners.

Now, I may be a little overzealous, but I think sharing the information will help further establish a level of authority with the students, especially showing the students how their teacher has a mastery of the subject being taught and can explain in precise detail why an assignment falls short or reaches new heights. This could help prevent, or even eliminate, any punitive consequence because the students will respect a teacher who knows what they are talking about, showing the students the teachers is coming from a place of caring about a student's performance. The teacher is not there just to collect a paycheck.

This is me just venting about everything going on in the class right now. Ignoring the areas that I find that can be improved (even though I have very little training), Mr. Cinch is doing a great job of at least getting the students to show up, even if they are completely bored while instruction is given.

Either way, I believe I am doing very well overall. I was complimented on the quality of the activities I am providing to the class during the first week, a welcome surprise. Another feather in my cap is my movement in the classroom. While the students are working on an assignment, I will float around the room to make sure they understand what Mr. Cinch is asking, and I will coach them accordingly.

Also, I love how I can integrate technology into the classroom. For example, we were supposed to read a short story, and I found a 13-minute, fan-made animation corresponding to work. I was able to share it with the class, allowing the students to take a moment to internalize what was going on in the story, especially if the story was difficult for them to read.

I am glad my mentor teacher supports the way I am providing a varied approach for instruction. By seeing an animated version of the story, I believe the students are grasping the information even better, allowing them to draw deeper connections to the source material. Overall, the differentiation of how I teach the material will enable students of multiple learning styles and levels to fulfill the State Standards.

I am still a little bummed that Mr. Cinch will not allow me to take attendance, though. Apparently, his overall reasoning was a student intern like myself will only use the record-keeping aspects when I am student teaching, not interning. I hope this is just an impasse and not something that will harm me going forward.

Memory before the Arizona Teachers Academy

My favorite memory while living in hotels on Van Buren was the time the GOAL (Gifted Opportunities for Advanced Learners) program at David Crockett Elementary School received the opportunity to see Dr. Carl Sagan speak at America West Arena. That should be one of my most cherished memories, but the experience is tinged with a missed opportunity just moving beyond my grasp.

At the time, the America West Arena, now known as the Footprint Center, had a mainly grey exterior, lacking in most of the modern amenities that now adorn the arena. All the schools were huddled into seating sections that took up one-half of the seating area on both sides court. Because this was mostly a school function, the arena's interior where Dr. Sagan was supposed to speak was illuminated by naturally occurring sunshine. I guess the arena's ownership didn't want to waste any extra money on a public school event, even though it was likely a tax write-off for them.

As we entered the arena, walking through the double doors, I was mesmerized by the vastness of such a large arena. Even with all of the lights and everything else turned off to save electricity, it was the most strikingly beautiful moment I have ever seen in my young life, eclipsing any and all school and community center gyms. I especially enjoyed my chance to walk across the court to the rafters on the opposite end of the arena. The joy of walking across a basketball court where real professional basketball players get to play was a moment I wouldn't trade for anything.

When my classmates, the teachers, and I got to our school's section, we had to ascend about 15 rows to find our seats, but it didn't matter because I would soon see one of the famous astrophysicists to ever live.

When I finally got to my seat, from Dr. Sagan's perspective, my group and I sat on the right side of his speaking platform. It was a typical platform used for presentations or award shows, and it was dark grey in color, but it would allow all of us, no matter where we sat, to get a good glimpse of the speaker. I don't know how long it went (since I didn't have a watch or anything), but I do know that was I wholly enthralled by everything he was talking about. As his words weaved the mental images in my head, I couldn't help but imagine what it would be like to walk upon an alien world.

Dr. Sagan, after giving his presentation to the entire group about the subject of our solar system, opened up questions for all of the students in attendance. The arena was packed with students from what felt like hundreds of schools, and we were near the top of the rafters on Dr. Sagan's right side, from his perspective, because he was standing at a podium on a makeshift stage near center court. I remember taking a moment to get the courage to go down there and ask him something profound because the other students from other schools were asking routine, low-level questions about what was the Earth made of or the age of the Sun.

Before this event, I was supposed to be studying for the State Geography Bee competition hosted at *The University*. Somehow, I was one of the only students from my school's GOAL who did well enough on the written test to be invited to compete at the state-level competition. So in preparation for the competition, our school's library would let me check out books and magazines like National Geographic to read, to memorize everything (or at least allow a functional level of familiarity so success would be within my reach). But, unfortunately, I would become distracted with other flights of fancy, even things about astronomy. I remember reading about the Hubble constant, the age of the universe, and how there was supposedly a conflict between astronomers regarding the theoretical age of the universe and how some of the observable stars far exceeded the universe's potential age.

Instead of preparing for a competition that could have potentially netted me a college scholarship, I fell down the rabbit hole of astronomical magazines. When my time came to wow someone from the actual scientific field, all the random information rapidly vibrating in my mind congealed for an opportunity to impress one of the most famous astronomers during my lifetime.

When I finally brought up the courage, when I finally utilized my baggage from my feeling like I was less than, I decided I needed to go down there and ask a question that may wow even Dr. Sagan. The roach-infested-hotel-room-sized chip on my shoulder screamed at me to go down there.

I would show 'em.

I would show them this unwashed child had abilities that a cursory look could not reveal. I took careful, light steps as I went down the rafters with the faint hope of impressing a great mind like his. But, as I was taking each step down to the floor, a steady stream of potential questions ran through my mind: "why do you believe there is a difference between the perceived age of the universe and some of the stars being older? Could this lend to the belief that the universe expands and contracts, and some of those stars leftovers from previous iterations of our universe?"

I crossed the court, all the eyes of hundreds of students looking down upon me.

I stepped in line. I was the last one.

There were three others ahead of me.

"What is the most abundant element on Earth?"

"Oxygen."

Two.

"How long will the Sun burn hydrogen?"

"—About five billion years."

One. I was the next person in line.

"Why did you say we were made up of the star stuff?"

"Our star is likely a third-generation star, so after each one of those stars died, exploded, those heavy elements were spread all through what would become our solar system. Then, when all of those elements cooled enough, they formed planets. So, yes. We are made up of star-stuff."

After he answered this student's question, I ran through how to ask my question without sounding like a buffoon.

I walked up to the podium.

One of his associates stopped me.

"Okay, that's all our time. I know you all have great and insightful questions, but we don't have more time to answer them. So, I am sorry, but I hope you all had a wonderful time hearing about the universe."

That concluded my only opportunity to ask him a question. I can only look back and say, "what if?" and allow it to fade into background noise like the microwave remnants of the Big Bang. It is still measurable, the explosion long since concluded, but I can only use that moment to measure how far I have come as a person. I can no longer go back and change that course, step a little faster, get out of my seat a little earlier, unfortunately.

August 28th, 2018

Even if I only come out here one day a week, the sojourn out here is draining away any positive vibes about the experience.

The drive.

The stop-and-go traffic.

The near misses when drivers cut me off.

I am spending so much money on gas. It takes about two gallons every week, one each way. I mean, it helps the temperature is not sweltering in the morning, saving on gas burned to run the car's AC, but the drive really eats up gas and puts unneeded miles on my car in the process. My wallet really feels these long trips. Mr. Cinch stated that he doesn't mind the drive so much because he lives in Chandler. The money he makes here more than makes up for the time that he wastes driving all the way to work.

"Knowing I get enough to pay for everything dries all the tears I have every morning. The quiet drive home is always a bit relaxing. Sometimes, I will avoid the freeways so I can extend my trip as long as possible." So, I guess he has a rational approach to the situation, but I find it a bit condescending since I am doing this for free. Also, I don't have money to dry my tears, just the fear of debt.

When I enter the classroom, I take my seat in the back of the class to observe. According to Mr. Cinch, I shouldn't really interact with the students because I will not be in his classroom for that long, and he doesn't want the students to bring up his teacher intern whenever he tasks them with some assignment. The students will think it is unfair, complain, and lose track of the entire purpose of going to school. In other words, he doesn't want to be considered the bad guy whenever the students do not want to do anything—which is often the case since many of the students try and do play on their phones all the time, especially in class.

As I walk around the classroom, getting used to the surroundings, second-hour walks in. They seem pretty happy for the most part. I guess their last class was pretty enjoyable overall. The students sit down in lecture-style rows where the teacher is at the front, and the incoming group fills up all the rows.

From the way the class is being situated, the students are supposed to sit idle and partake of the curriculum the teacher provides — like they are lawn ornaments or something. Unfortunately, since I have been here, I think Mr. Cinch lulls the students to sleep with his lectures.

All of them.

All.

Of.

Them…

…has been tearfully boring with his anemic delivery, if I would call it that. It reminds me of Mr. Nix, one of my old math teachers back when I attended high school. He couldn't teach math at all. Also, he often lost his temper and yelled at us when we didn't listen. I guess he was showing us "tough love," as he liked to put it.

As much as I could remember from Mr. Nix's stories, he was an accountant for some corporation. When he got tired of doing the whole accounting gig, he fell into becoming a teacher. Regretfully, despite his best intention and outside information he provided to the students to connect to the importance of everything he was teaching, delivery was never really his skill, and his class was always mind-numbingly dull. If the act of watching paint dry could transform into a physical, tangible experience, Mr. Nix's class would be it.

So, when I say Mr. Cinch's delivery was a bit lacking, I would consider that a gross underestimate. Even with the lack of delivery, lack of personality, I found that Mr. Cinch had students that simply adored his delivery. *God only knows why.* I guess it is nothing more than a case of Stockholm syndrome, or the students are just playing the game until they graduate. After all, if they cross one teacher, they may cross all teachers because they often make small talk about problem students in the teachers' lounge.

Legally, teachers are not allowed to do discuss students with other teachers because it violates FERPA ("Family Education Rights and Privacy Act), but when no one tells, and there is no policing agent to make sure teachers act according to the law, they can do whatever they want as long as no witnesses are willing to come forward or testify. That is one of the primary reasons students are not allowed in the teachers' lounge for any reason. By giving students access to the lounge, these wildcards may potentially cause legal problems to come to light. It is already bad enough how teachers already have a long history of being sexually inappropriate with students or even spreading opposition research about students and families who may cause a problem. So, I guess this is why the school administrators set up safe spaces for teachers to gossip about students without fear of repercussion.

Either way, I was tasked with only sitting in the back of the classroom, observing what was going on. Whenever I would get up and start walking around the room, getting a feel of the overall layout to eventually deliver instruction to my own class later in the semester, I was told promptly told to sit down.

By doing this, Mr. Cinch robbed me of any authority while also making me appear weak and inadequate to the students. So, I wouldn't just sit down and watch. Instead, I would take notes on how the teacher delivered his lesson to emulate in my own classroom while writing down ways to change my instruction from his.

I did learn one important thing, even though Mr. Cinch was perfectly healthy, he liked to just sit at his desk, yelling at the students whenever they were not following directions or when he caught them on their cellphones whenever they were bored. I guess he didn't like expelling extra energy to monitor the students, making sure they stayed on task. It kind of makes sense, though. Since the school has so many students in the classroom, it would be a little difficult for him to move around. As a result, he might bump into a student, and that mistake could potentially be taken the wrong way — perhaps causing him to receive a reprimand from the administration.

On a side note, Mr. Cinch offered to give me more practice student teaching (in preparation for next semester) by coming to his class Monday through Friday, during every period. According to him, I should take an opportunity like this to receive as much practice as possible because I will be the one who makes all the classroom decisions next school year. I will not have anyone to fall back on while the kids patiently wait for me to deliver instruction (or they are bored with the topic of the lesson).

Part of me wants to take him up on the offer, but I also realize that I have a full schedule of classes. I don't have enough time to devote to lesson planning for Mr. Cinch's five classes and do all of the necessary work for my program. It is very tempting, but I kind of feel like this is a way for me to do all of his work for him. So why would my mentor teacher, the person who is supposed to mold me into being the best possible teacher I can be, offer me to take over all of his classes? Is there an ulterior motive around his offer?

I don't know. It was strongly suggested by Mr. Cinch, but I am just an intern. He is actually paid to show up there. I am only here one day a week. So, why would I want to subject myself to an unnecessary expansion of my responsibilities just to placate my mentor teacher? Mr.

Cinch is not taking 18 credits of Masters-level classes. Even though it is broken into two sections of nine credits, this is still a lot of work for a full-time graduate student without doing most of his work planning for every one of his classes on top of delivering the instruction.

He told me how taking over his class was the best thing for me. His spiel was the benefits of him watching while I was teaching his class. He would sit back and take notes on my progress and areas I could improve in. However, part of me thinks he would do the same thing as some of his students do and just doodle the hours away. I mean, extra practice is good, but I don't know if being exploited is the best thing for me professionally.

If I am there five days a week, for almost six hours a day, how would I have time to do any of the other material that I need to learn for my 500-level classes?

I know Mr. Cinch has a master's degree, but I think he received his while he was already working; so, I don't know if what he is trying to pull is even fair or comparable at all. I definitely do not think any of my fellow cohort members are exploring anything relating to working a full-time teaching schedule while not receiving a dime in compensation.

There is a reason *The University* saves full-time student teaching for our Spring Semester when we are all done with most of our education classes. The focus during the Spring Semester is gathering the absolute best data for the applied project required for the master's degree. We also gain practical experience teaching approved curriculum while also having the support so we can learn by failing. Because these students are tested at the end of the year, I wouldn't want to harm the progress of all the students because I will not be at this school in the spring nor will I be able to fully devote myself to their success.

I believe this is the overall purpose of our jobs, right? Taxpayers fund our salaries so we can prepare the students for the careers available when they graduate. Or better yet, we also give them the overall talent and self-assuredness to start their own businesses and help shape the communities where they live.

So, I hope this all works out. According to the feedback I have received so far, I have been complimented on going above and beyond by attending the English Department's Professional Learning Community (PLC) meetings while also showing my overall compassion for the students. Furthermore, because I attend PLC meetings when it's not required for a student intern, I believe my extra effort in mastering the career will help me get my foot into the door with this school district next year. If nothing else, this additional activity will provide me with connections that will help me in the teachers' job market. This is of course ignoring Mr. Cinch's ludicrous offer to allow myself to be exploited by him by working his job while he gets paid.

In my experience so far, the PLC meetings were pretty easy for me since I'm just interning. I just come in early on the Professional Development days, sit down, and listen to how they plan for the lessons for the rest of the week. They also bring up random low, medium, and high-level student answers to explore how students grasp the content based on their ability level and they adjust instruction based on the data they all gather.

From my perspective as a student intern, if they were to ask for any type of contribution from me, considering I am just watching Mr. Cichy do his thing, my contribution to the group would basically run like this: *I cannot do anything but sit there and watch Mr. Cinch's classroom.* That's it. That's all I could ever contribute to the group in my current capacity.

Part of me wants to really get my hands dirty, even though I only come in one day a week. I just think everyone in the class will find it a bit more refreshing hearing me deliver the instruction instead of just listening to Mr. Cinch pontificate about the ins-and-outs of how English is so gosh darn awesome (in a completely monotone voice).

From what I know, people shouldn't just learn by watching, unable to interact. It does not provide an opportunity for growth or development. A teacher cannot truly become a teacher by confinement to sit on the sidelines. It is the same as a professional athlete or other doctors.

I'll learn by doing — within reason.

I think this is a way for getting back at me for not taking him up on his offer. He wants to put me further and further behind because I would not make his Fall Semester that much easier.

I don't know if he did this with other student interns, but I think it is widely inappropriate to try and take advantage of someone that is just looking up to him for guidance on being the best teacher possible.

I hope he doesn't keep me in neutral for the remainder of the semester I will be forced to be in charge of the entire class next semester as a student teacher, and I will lack the tool of experience, even if it is minute. If I don't get the real opportunity to succeed, I will never have my chance to prove my mettle.

I guess I am just getting too anxious. I cannot just sit idly by and watch the world go by. I think I will just wait for my chance to shine.

Memory before the Arizona Teachers Academy

Memories, they can be funny things. Even though I remember the peaceful time for my family living in St. Petersburg, Florida, even though most of my pre-seven-year-old memories were mostly viewed with rose-colored glasses, I know of a pair of experiences that dulled the sheen of my childhood. Both of them happened before I was able to even attend kindergarten.

The first one, I was three years old, and my younger sibling was about two. We lived inside a trailer park. I remember the giant trees towering overhead that would provide shade when it was exceptionally hot. Because the massive trees were blocking out sunlight, there wasn't really any grass on the ground, mostly dirt.

Looking back, the shade from the massive trees killed all the grass in the area. If the owner of the trailer park really waned grass in the area, he would likely need to trim the limbs of the trees or remove them all together. Because the trees were so massive, so tall, there was really nothing to be done.

Because of all the dirt and dust on the ground, my sibling and I got very dirty on a regular basis. We would both track all the filth from the outside world into the trailer. We would subsequently get it all over everything like the furniture and our beds. So, my Mom made a regular habit of making sure we were properly clean after we played outside.

One time, though, my mom put both of us in the bathtub to clean-away any and all mud or dirt. It was just an ordinary bubble bath, and it was so fun to just relax in the warm water, play around with our toys like little boats and rubber duckies that would squeak when you pressed on them very hard. We were young, and we were free of responsibilities.

When the bath was done, I raced to be the first one out. As I got out of the tub, a ton of water likely splashed all over the place, making the floor very slick. My balance gave way, and I slipped. Pain shot through my right butt cheek. I got up and began running and screaming through the trailer, out the front door, and in tight circles in the dusty ground in front, naked as the day I was born. I ran back into the trailer and belly-flopped on my parents' bed — still kicking and screaming my head off.

My mom came in to comfort me and wiped away the steady stream of excruciating pain flowing down my young face. Evidently, there was an exposed bolt holding the toilet in place in the bathroom. When I jumped out and slipped, the bolt, crusted with rust and covered with tetanus, ripped a nice gash in the exposed skin of my right cheek.

As I was still whining and crying about my misfortune, my parents took me to the emergency room to get the wound looked at while also making sure that I could receive another dose of the DTP (Diphtheria-Tetanus-Pertussis) vaccine. Because of the mortality rate of tetanus and the potential of long-term problems from the disease, my parents did not want play Viral Russian Roulette with my life. Also, my parents wanted to make sure everything was okay, and I receive prompt stitches for the gash because there was blood everywhere.

After going through the waiting room of the emergency room, I was taken back to be seen by the doctors. The nurse had me lay down on my stomach, and she told me that I would feel a slight pinch and the pain would go away. The local anesthesia quickly took hold, and I did not feel anything while they stitched up the small two-inch gift from the toilet's exposed bolt. When I completed the entire ordeal of getting my posterior stitched up, they put a giant bandage on my butt and sent me back home.

The other negative story was more of a bookend to my time in Florida. When I was about five years old, a few weeks before my family left Florida to make a permanent stop in Arizona instead of moving all the way to California to be closer to my grandmother, who lived in Marina Del Ray at the time, my Dad decided to go and visit one of his friends. It was late at night, pitch black because it was a New Moon, and I couldn't really see anything. So, in hindsight, my Dad picked a perfect opportunity to go and visit someone's house.

Because my brain was a few decades away from full maturation due to me only being five years old, my impulsivity stemming from my lack of maturity caused me to throw caution to the wind because I was safe with my parents, and we were visiting a place my Dad vouched for. So, as I ran up to the friend's front door, I stopped right in front to open the door, jumping with anticipation of what would be inside. Seconds later, what felt like a mere blink of the eye, I thought a moment of the mundane became memorable.

I started feeling sharp pitching and burning all over my body, legs, arms, back, cheek, and the back of my neck. This pain was different than being pricked by a needle when getting a shot or having my blood drawn. This pain had heat behind it. Unfortunately for my young-self, I had stepped on a fire ant mound that was right in front of the guy's house.

I started screaming, running into the back of my parents' station wagon, and began drenching myself from the water we kept in the backseat of the car (in case the radiator was overheating), what felt like a vain attempt to wash away my tormentors. The pain continued to flow across the surface of my skin. This unbearable pain and burning seared its way into my memory. Ants, especially fire ants, were serious business. These little devils bit my young, exposed flesh. The stings from the ants' solenopsin venom exploded into torrents of agony across every one of my nerve endings. The torment quickly carved a lasting memory into my psyche.

I screamed, yelled, and cried deeply as the water became my only focus, my only sense of salvation — a light at the end of the tunnel. I cleansed myself in a strictly literal sense. Unfortunately for my parents, the process to rid me of this invasive species caused the entire back seat to be completely soaked. But I didn't care. The pain was gone, and I was just tired from what felt like hours of pain.

As what was likely my last hurrah within the state, fate wanted this experience to be as physically and emotionally damaging as possible. There was nothing wrong with Florida, but I wasn't too keen on a return for years because of this experience. Even if I wanted to go back, it didn't matter due to the lack of finances preventing us from returning there for a long, long time.

To this day, my Dad still talks about returning to Florida. Maybe he will get a chance once I become a teacher and have money to send him back there.

October 16th, 1998,

    YES!

    I made it through the midpoint of my internship. Overall, I really feel like everything in the program is going very well. However, I believe my placement is kind of meh. I just sit in the back and observe. Then, when I get a little antsy, twirling my thumbs in anticipation for something engaging, I start moving around the classroom to make sure the students are working on their assignments, asking them if they need assistance. I did this, even though Mr. Cinch told me not to do it earlier in my internship. As I have been advancing through the semester, I notice something pretty peculiar. I think he doesn't care anymore.

    When it comes to what he does, the person who is supposed to be my mentor just stays at his desk all day. For some reason, I think his students would stay on task longer if he was more involved instead of just yelling at them from behind his desk. I guess Mr. Cinch has been doing this for much longer than me; so, it kind of makes sense if he lost the will to really commit to what it takes to be an excellent teacher.

    The students are entirely at his whims, though. He brings down the hammer when they act up too much. So, in a way, the young adults may be the victims of whatever motivates his flights of fancy or the punishing retribution that may come down like a bolt of lightning from the heavens at any particular moment. I think a lot of this, though, stems from just sitting on his ass and teaching via a slideshow.

    Even though my time at this placement will be coming to an end in a few weeks, I really feel for these students. My heart truly aches. I see so limitless possibilities houses within their young eyes, but I also realize their teacher's inaction is slowly robbing them of their motivation. Their hope. They didn't ask for this. I know the students have no control over where they are placed by the school's administration. All I can do is hope for the best.

When I finish this internship and move on to my next adventure, I will carry the hope of the new classroom not being as bad as this one. They are 12th Graders, on the cusp of living their own lives and transitioning to the job market or going to college next school year, I hope this experience doesn't sour them completely towards education since that is the only way many of them will be able to escape from poverty.

But, if I was given the opportunity to continue to drive out here, I would not take it. I would beg to be placed somewhere closer. The drive is way too far, gas is too expensive to justify interning or even student teaching at this location. I will only seriously consider finding a position at this school if I am able to get a guaranteed job (since this district one of the best paying ones in the entire state). The extra money and the outstanding students, and a community is in so much need, is something that will really entices me, but I don't want to limit myself to just one site. I will have plenty of options for employment.

Either way, I am curious how full-time student teaching is going to treat me. I hope my teaching site is much closer to my house. I enjoyed helping the students, but I will not miss the soul-crushing commute and having to kiss precious hours of sleep good-bye. I mean, who will *really* enjoys giving away more than two hours of their time just to travel to a school in a different city, remain unpaid, and feel like their contribution only makes the other teacher's life a bit easier?

I have been told how this training would prepare me for taking over a classroom when I am done with the program, but if I am not prepared adequately to run my own class, my students will suffer the most. Still, I feel the lack of help or assistance from Mr. Cinch is causing a delay in my training. We are going completely off script because he just wants to be lazy. I hope I am not too far back when I start my student teaching at a new school next year.

When the program drafted the requirements for the class, I highly doubt *The University's* College of Education had mentor teachers like him in mind. Maybe I should just call him Mr. Zilch because that is how much help he is giving me (nah, it isn't worth the effort). I mean he should be better, especially if he is taking on the responsibility of helping out the future teachers.

Could this be based on my denial of giving him a mini-vacation? It makes me wonder, but I think it could also be indicative of the system he was molded into.

Mr. Cinch did share a story a few weeks ago about how his mentor teacher took advantage of him, making him do all the work under the guise of training. He stated that when he was student teaching, the mentor teacher would just give him a packet of what was being covered throughout the internship period. Then, his mentor teacher tasked him with writing all the lesson plans for every class during the entire experience. It sounded like infamous mentor teacher didn't really want to work and unloaded all the paid job responsibilities onto a young student teacher. The behavior was being repeated, and I was supposed to smile and gladly do his job.

As I began to feel empathy (and even a little bit of sympathy), I realized that his long game was to con me into taking over his job responsibilities. He could relax, kick his feet up, and crack up the proverbial beer while watching me do all of his work.

If I messed up (or the students didn't perform as well), he could just blame it all on me. But if the students did outperformed expectations, he would gladly take all of the credit for my hard work.

Now, I can see why some teachers really want to be mentor student teachers. Theoretically, a student intern or student teacher may allow the mentor to take a form of paid vacation. Thus, the mentor teacher receives full pay while doing a small fraction of their contractual responsibilities. This unspoken agreement between universities and public schools should really bother me, but it doesn't. It's just the nature of the beast. Still, I need to focus on doing the best I can to finish this program, graduate, and transition to my own classroom and a life where I am paid to pass along the State-approved information to the my own classroom full of students.

On the bright side, Mr. Cinch gave me a glowing recommendation for my evaluation. However, I am pissed about how I was marked down because I could not take attendance. How will I take attendance if my mentor teacher just stays at his desk all day and will not move at the beginning of class? How am I supposed to do an activity he states as a deficit when he will not even give me the room to accomplish such a task? Is he expecting me to use his computer through telekinesis? I mean, if I had this sort of power or ability, I sure as hell would not be trying to be a teacher. I would be doing something much more helpful for humanity or even more profitable. With such extraordinary power, I would could even work for the military or something to help make sure our country was protected against major threats.

I guess he is taking his anger out on me because he volunteered to give up his preparation period to takeover an 11th Grade class that lost its teacher. Evidently, the teacher quit because of the way she was being mistreated by the students. I heard from one of the other employees from the school how some of the students in that teacher's class were emotionally and physically violent, and the school didn't really do enough to mitigate that level and form of disruption. So, Mr. Cinch took the class over because he would receive a 20% pay raise for teaching the class.

If I was in his shoes, I don't know if I would do it.

Well, I definitely will not have such a schedule when I am first starting out. I will love my prep periods to prepare for the rest of the classes for the day. A 6/5th schedule would surely add a level of extra burnout from the extra 20% increase in work that comes from having a 20% increase in pay. If I was in his shoes, I don't think I will sacrifice family time for what will amount to a few thousand dollars more, but I guess that is just me.

Memory before the Arizona Teachers Academy

As the Sun was blazing overhead, beating down in the late morning of a typical Monday, I was picked up from my studio apartment by the van that transported patients to my rehabilitation facility. It was just one of my normal days off because I was still on short-term disability, meaning I could not show up to work without a medical release, or I could potentially lose my job.

I could have driven to rehab if I had my license, but I was told at the hospital that because I suffered a severe traumatic brain injury, I would be unable to drive because my driver's license was medically suspended. The only way for me to ever get my license back was to go through rehabilitation and pay for a formal driving evaluation. If I passed the evaluation, then I would potentially get my license back. Since I did not have enough money at the time to pay for the services nor a car, I was stuck with getting transport to and from my house by the Arizona's Premier Rehabilitation Center van service.

James, the company's middle-aged driver, always arrived at 9 AM to pick me up because I was the only person he picked up at that early. He was a pretty nice guy, and he would always have a smile on his face when I got in the van. I would also have plenty of time to talk with him about everything going on in the world because of my natural curiosity. Additionally, it's kind of uncomfortable to be driven around in a van without saying a word to the driver. I learned he was from Milwaukee, Wisconsin. He decided to move out here to escape the cold winters of the Northern United States. He even said how he liked bragging to his family about having pool parties during the Thanksgiving holiday.

When we arrived, James would park the van at the entrance to let me out. He had to make sure that I went inside and checked in for my outpatient care. Signing-In at the front desk was a strict requirement for services because there needed to be a record that I showed up for service. Evidently, my signature was the record of the facility administering treatment, allowing them to track how many times I showed up before billing the State. It was the only way Arizona would release any pay any money to APR.

I really enjoyed what the program represented. Vocational Rehabilitation would train the people to get back into the workforce instead of keeping a person at home and filing for disability payments. Since I already had a job at CDC-INFO and was just on short-term disability, they wanted to ensure no detriments were preventing me from keeping my job. Apparently, my tendency of telling abusive callers my unauthorized closing statement got me into trouble. I guess it was not okay for me to say, "I cannot diagnose you over the phone. If you are asking me to diagnose you instead of getting tested, you can get the same effect by just asking a random person on the street if you have HIV or not."

So, it didn't take much talking or convincing to receive the benefits from Arizona because they are already had the record of my traumatic brain injury (since I was placed on the state-funded insurance).

Walking into the lunchroom at APR's North Phoenix office, I pull my self-packed lunch out of the refrigerator. I just packed a bologna sandwich, a soda, and some regular potato chips. My lunch would basically be called pitiful by anyone except those who were starving (like myself) because I was living off of short-term disability from my current job, but it was enough to make me feel complete, whole — for the most part.

I would look at my fellow patients, my fellow brain injury survivors, and I would just wonder how they got into the same situation as me. One of them was a person who suffered a stroke, and they came to the outpatient services to receive additional therapy and other quality of life assistance. Another patient was seeking services because he had a drug overdose or something, choked on his own vomit, and was eventually revived by a family member who was also an EMT. Unluckily for him, he suffered a severe brain injury due to oxygen deprivation because his vomit obstructed his airway for around three minutes. So, the rehabilitation center was a place for him to re-learn some of his.lost skills.

Whenever I was at lunch, no one ever really talked. All the patients kind of kept to themselves, minding their own business. I would look around, seeing if anyone was open for discussion, but it never amounted to anything. I wound up just eating my lunch while thinking about the next stages of my life. What would I do? Would I stay at CDC-INFO forever? What kind of skills did a mid-20s adult with only a high school diploma possess?

The questions would swirl, feeding into one another because the lack of stimuli, the lack of anything seizing my attention was really annoying. My brain injury washed away all of my social pragmatics (one of the reasons the State was willing to pay for my program). I would be nervous, impatient, and grow anxious when I was left to stew in my own thoughts. Also, I couldn't sit still. In a way, a symptom of a traumatic brain injury could cause the development of Attention-Deficit/Hyper Activity disorder because the pathways in the brain have been disrupted by the diffuse axonal injury, the left frontal lobe hemorrhage, and/or the subarachnoid hemorrhage.

So, after lunch, I participated in another round of rehab with John, one of the resident physical therapists. Typically, physical therapy is just work, and it is kind of dull. But one session really stood out from all the other times that faded into background memories. It was all because of one moment of something unexpected happening that caused it to be etched into my memories.

The one session was a pretty good round of physical therapy. Near the end, I did something I really believe is pretty funny and inspiring. John wanted to test my reflexes and my ability to maintain a standing posture. After all the other usual physical therapy stuff, the therapist wanted to measure my overall ability to catch myself when I was falling (considering I face-planted a month ago at the county hospital).

The therapy to test my reflexes was straightforward overall, relying upon gravity to really test my abilities. First, I was supposed to straighten up as tall as possible while also tipping to one side. Next, I would put all of my weight on his outstretched hand, leaning on the very corner of the outside edge of my foot. In this case, it was on my right side and my right foot. My left foot was a few inches off the ground, pressed firmly against the left side of my right foot. If someone took a picture of me at that very moment, I would look like I was standing at attention but titled to the right. After I leaned all the way over, John would remove his hand, and I was supposed to correct my balance to catch myself. If I failed, my limbs slowed by brain trauma, and unable to stop my swift descent into the hard floor, I would comically crash to the floor. John's insurance to me was him immediately outstretching an arm or his hand to catch me and keep me from slamming the right-side of my head into the hard floor.

So, I leaned on his hand, terrified that I would fall. I looked straight ahead to see the bench, the beds, and the posters promoting physical therapy as a pathway to a positive life post-injury. Feeling his hand supporting my weight, I was still uneasy about crashing onto the tile floor and busting my head wide open. The potential ramifications if I slammed headfirst into the hard ground would have likely resulted in a comical danger sign appearing behind my back, letting the viewers at home know that I was in trouble. I believed John knew what

68

could potentially happen, and he was prepared for everything.

The PT would catch me, right?

My breath was sporadic in anticipation.

Body tense, rigid.

One moment passed.

I was still suspended, all weight leaning to the right. Every possible result ran through my head.

If I fell now, would John's reaction be fast enough to even catch me? Would my falling body slip from his grasp? Would I be knocked out from the force of crashing into the floor? Would they send me home early if I messed up during physical therapy?

So many thoughts racing forward with each progressive moment, each worse than the last, caused my body to tighten up in anticipation of a future where I tumbled.

Would the force cause another hemorrhage? Was my head so fragile that another blunt force trauma would be the moment when my proverbial actors left the stage?

He removed his hand.

With a quickness, I step down forcibly to my right to catch myself. The force was so quick, so sudden, John was not prepared. I stepped directly on the bridge of his foot — right on the tongue of their right shoe. My almost instantaneous reaction caused the therapist to let out a surprised yell.

My quick reaction was supposedly unexpected during the exercise for someone who survived a severe traumatic brain injury — axons were torn asunder, hemorrhages everywhere. Yet, with my fall into the pavement in front of the hospital only a few months in my rear-view, I was taken aback by my sudden swiftness.

Where was this before? Did I learn from the mistake? Did I recover some of my reactive nature post-injury? Or did the physical therapist move slowly to build

69

up my sense of confidence in me, faith in what I was
capable of?

I never found out the truth from that moment, if my reaction time was faster than his, but I was still proud of what I could do. Part of the entire rehab process is to reconstruct the sense of self-reliance in the injured person. With the confidence, they may be able to better recover than those who are depressed or have a negative outlook on their condition…

Or I could just be fortunate because the damage occurred within areas that did not cause long-term disability. After all, a traumatic brain injury is like a snowflake. The way we are all affected is different. Some never wake from comas. Some never can string together a coherent sentence. Some are Phineas Gage. Some live long, productive lives without a ramification that severs life's candlewick. All the others fall somewhere in between.

November 9th, 2018

As I make the drive down to the school, the Sun isn't even peeking through a smattering of clouds to say hello at such an early hour (6:00 AM). Thankfully, the highway is not especially busy right now. The Piestewa Freeway winds north-south from Loop 101 in Phoenix, curving west around Shea Blvd, and resuming the mostly north-south route around Northern Ave. until it merges with Interstate 10 (I-10) in Phoenix. I then take I-10 W towards Los Angeles, exit onto the Interstate 17 Freeway South, exit at 19th Avenue, and travel the rest of the way by surface streets towards LIHS.

Even though the drive to the school is incredibly long, the temperatures in the mid-70s makes everything alright. I don't have to run the AC because it isn't as hot as hell. The serenity of being alone during the long drive places me in the right frame of mind for my classes and dealing with a less than ideal mentor, meaning I am not really worrying myself since the main problem is not being allowed to do anything but just sit in the back of the room, bored. I just show up, metaphorically *clock in*, and I assume my position in the back of the room, ensuring the students stay on task and do everything that needs to be done.

I only have one month left in this internship. Pretty soon, I will get a new school in a school district t that is closer to my house. The drive shouldn't be as long. The commute to an unpaid position will not be as draining, vacuuming out any sense of enjoyment as I learn such an essential profession. I honestly believe *The University* sent me out to the middle of nowhere to remind me of the sacrifices of being a teacher. I surmise this is the only logical deduction given the available information, right? I know none of the fellow members of my cohort have to drive as far as me; so, I guess I am learning the hard lesson.

With Mr. Cinch *still* preventing me from fully participating in the day-to-day requirements during my weekly visit, my thoughts turn why he is treating me like this, disrespecting the program to such an extent. I believe some of this comes from me not taking over his classes full-time for the semester. I guess for someone that has been teaching here for multiple years, he was trying to use me as someone to make his life easier. He wanted to turn the 2018 Fall Semester into his paid vacation where he would do the minimal amount of work while benefitting from an increased $6/5^{th}$ salary. He literally wrote me up for not attending all of the afterschool meetings, not working with a PLC, and even said I need to work on my ability to teach students (even though he is not letting me teach students).

Like…what?!

I am just a student intern. It is not my job to come in five days a week. All my fellow members of my cohort told me not to take him up on his offer because Mr. Cinch was trying to be gelatinous blob, consuming my free time and converting my tears of frustration into his more leisurely first-half of the school year. He just wants to collect his salary while doing the least amount of work possible. God, the way he tried to sell this to me as a way to benefit me as opposed to him? What a load of horse shit! His dishonesty knows no bounds. He even said that checking my lessons, making sure they were correct and aligned to what he desires for the students to learn this school year, requires way more time and energy than doing the work. In other words, he just told me that just looking over my stuff is more work than doing his job. Yeah, he's doing me such a big, fucking favor!

He wanted me to do his whole job for him? I was born at night, but I was sure as hell not born last night. I don't know. I just need to keep my eye on the prize and finish out this month as quickly as possible. I only have to come out here four more times, so I should just let the relaxation of completing the week wash over me, refocus myself, preparing for the final stretch ahead.

I should really talk to my fellow cohort members to see if they are experiencing the same thing. This doesn't seem right to try to take advantage of someone trying to learn to be a teacher. If a teacher really wants to take a day off, they should use their sick days or something. The career is protected by a teacher's contract and often a teachers' union to ensure the contractual agreement is followed to the letter, allowing them to have a little more leeway when a contract employee decides to utilize their own personal time.

Could Mr. Cinch be using a poorly veiled attempt to reduce his workload and allow him to save up his personal days to receive a larger paycheck at the end of the year? Talk about "having your cake and eating it too." I heard that *The School District* provides a lump sum payment for any sick and vacation overage a teacher has at the end of each contract, so I guess his actions make sense. I mean, Mr. Cinch received a law degree before switching over to his teaching career. So maybe he is pretty apt at knowing how to game the system. Nothing like maximizing the benefit of a student teacher while also limiting the work.

Pretty soon, it will not be my problem.

Memory before the Arizona Teachers Academy

After moving into our new house, I hired a pest control company to spray our house and lay down traps to catch bugs or whatever pest was trying to proverbially squat in our garage. The house was near a nature preserve, so I rationalized the decision to hire someone to spray literal poison in our garage due to the possibility of a wild vermin invasion. It didn't help that I saw an adult scorpion walk down my bedroom hallway after we had a bed delivered by a furniture store. I imagined the scorpion was strutting its stuff towards the bathroom, thinking it was the boss of the house. I showed him! I threw a few things at it. The impact of the first item caused it to get into the defensive position, ready to strike whatever came to close. I finally hit it with the bottom of my boot I threw at it. I quickly walked over to the downed victim and crushed the life out of it. The little bastard would no longer have a chance to harm me.

I care about living things and how they will help keep my house pest-free, but scorpions were something I would not even attempt to mess with or even keep in our house. There form of pest control is non-discriminatory between bugs and humans. They could potentially control the human population in my home, and I didn't waste good money for a house to be practically unlivable for anyone but the most daring. Also, I may be young, but I was not that young to mess around with a scorpion invasion. Now, I know they are pretty tough to kill — existing as little unstoppable killing machines, so I need to kill the food source. If the food source was gone, those little bastards would find more fertile pastures to feed.

I looked on my phone to find a good pest exterminator in my area that also would come out on short notice. I was in luck. I would only have to wait a few days, and they would come down, give me a quote, and they would set me up for regular spraying. The initial inspection went without a hitch, and they gave me a fair offer to come in seasonally to use non-harsh compounds to rid the area of a food source for scorpions. With the food source gone, the scorpions would take off. No more concern about potentially dying from a scorpion sting.

When it came time to finally do the treatment, the pest exterminator company came into our house, investigated the possible infestation of any and all livable spaces, and they sprayed everywhere, making sure to put down enough poison to send any bugs to their doom, especially near the dog door that was in the master bedroom.

I was also given a handful of glue traps for ground squirrels. Evidently, the wiring harness for the electrical in my car's electrical system mimicked the touch and taste of the wood those little assholes use to file down their teeth (a very costly repair). So, those little beauties were placed in the garage as my gift to them.

Of the two traps in the garage, one was on the left side of the garage along the wall and near the main garage door sensor. There was a little u-nook between the door and the left-side of the wall. On the other side of the garage near the extra garage door for the three-car garage, I placed the other trap near the matching nook. With everything in place to force away any bugs in the area, I never saw another scorpion on the property as long as we lived there. I felt immense satisfaction with the knowledge the stinging bastard's food source was going MIA, and I was not going to catch a random scorpion that would kill any one of us.

While the invertebrates never bothered me while I lived there, I did catch two snakes on the glue traps in the garage. The first one was a garter snake, and the other one was a king snake. The first one happened right after we started our service. The second one was a few months before we sold the house and moved to another part of town.

With the garter snake, I was by myself because I was working on college shit and my partner was at work at the time. At the time, I was still working on my undergraduate degrees. I heard the warning from the security system, letting me know there was movement in the garage. When I went in there to find out, as sure as shit I saw I caught a snake that was trapped on the glue trap. The little bugger was on the right side of the garage, well beyond the right nook, and it was twisting as hard as it could to remove itself from the sticky bondage. Its head was stuck on the glue trap while the rest of its body was free to twist and turn in an attempt to escape.

I also didn't notice a rattler on the fucker, meaning the threat of two poisonous fangs were ruled out. It also lacked the black, red, and yellow markings on its body, meaning it also wasn't a coral snake. My automatic fear of it being potentially poisonous dissipated. I memorized the markings and colors of the snake, slightly light brown, and I pulled out my phone to see what it could be. From the pictures and the descriptions on the web, I quickly deduced that it was just a garter snake. So, me being somewhat aware what snakes like that do help the environment, I decided it would be in my best interest to help free it from the clutches of the trap. Knowing my luck, if I did nothing, my home would have been invaded by something more of a problem than a simple wayward snake.

I opened my garage door. Additionally, I grabbed an extra metal security system sign left behind by the previous homeowner. I dragged the trap out of the garage and moved it on the sidewalk beyond the front of my house and my neighbor's, the snake was not happy with this move. I carefully walked along, hoping not to harm or frighten the little vermin catcher, and I stopped near the empty field behind both of our houses (where the nature preserve started). I deduced that a free snake would do more to help exterminate any vermin in the area with extreme prejudice better than a pest control company. This would be a lot more effective, environmentally friendly, and less financially draining than bringing the exterminators out here again to finish up the job.

So, I grabbed the opposite end of the trap (far from the snake's head), and I began to use the metal sign to pry the snake off the glue trap. I was oh so gentle because I did not want the snake to be hurt at all. If the snake was hurt, it would be less likely to actually kill anything in the area. I would have effectively let the snake go to die. I couldn't have that! I slowly and surely pried the snake away until only the last bit of its lower jaw was still stuck. I squeezed the metal sign under its chin, pulled up slightly, and the glue gave way, leaving the snake free to go along and mind its own business. Then I backed the fuck up as it slithered back underneath some bushes and I never saw it again.

For the king snake, my partner found it. They wanted to kill it, but I couldn't have that. So even though they were afraid, I convinced them that I knew how to save the snake without anyone getting harmed in the process. I followed the same exercise with the garter snake: identification, drag, and release. It was simple enough, and it helped make sure the surrounding nature would not be harmed even more by extensive chemicals.

In hindsight, I am glad that we sold the house and moved to a completely different area closer to the city. Even though the desert preserve and the sunsets were splendid, the minor problems with squirrels, snakes, spiders, and scorpions marred the overall experience. But either way, I can honestly say that I am proud of myself for making sure the area was as healthy as possible.

December 7th, 2018

Well, the end of my teacher internship is coming next week. I cannot even wait for the calendar to switch to 2019 and put this entire experience behind me. Nothing like a fruitless experience getting smaller and smaller in my rear-view. Considering I also did my full internship while also taking a full class schedule, I am proud of myself. I know it was just a taste and not everything that is waiting for me, but I am one step closer to having my own classroom. I will also be able to earn money and have a pension when I retire. I know it will not pay a lot, but money for retirement is always a good thing. Since the retirement package comes from the State of Arizona, I should be in an excellent position to receive retirement pay without fear of it being cut off. I mean, if it gets cut off, then I am in a whole lot worse shape than just worrying about a little pension.

One thing I will not miss, though, is the soul-draining drive. From wasting real money to just *attend* an unpaid internship to the possibility of getting into a car accident because of the atrocious rush hour drivers, I will be entirely at ease to never travel this far to go to work again. My goodness, the commute caused me to seriously reconsider ever being an educator if this was the only location that would hire me. However, by wasting hours just to sit in one single room that pays me no money, in an internship that pays me no money (because this is preparing me for my future profession), I hope the still have a zest for education even in the face of being minimized and disregarded by my own mentor.

I know time is a commodity, and I know *The University* and *The School District* robbed me of that time by placing me so far away, and I understand the drive was a way for me to see other students who do not live in my community, so I will not let this little hiccup keep me from my ultimate goal. Students need a quality education, and I have the skills and the fire to give it to them. Some students need more help than others, especially if they have teachers like my mentor teacher.

The students themselves are phenomenal. It was nice to help such young minds become a better version of themselves, setting themselves up to provide for their own future, carve their own path in our country. Yet, every week I come out, I can see the students' eyes pleading for a teacher who interacts with them instead of a teacher who just sits at their desk. I know the students come from a marginalized population, but I wonder how Mr. Cinch will act if one of the students possesses the courage to have their own *Jeff Bliss* moment. If more students would call out their teachers for doing the bare minimum, maybe I would be getting my hands dirty as an intern instead of just being a spectator.

I really wish I had more control, but I was only an intern. I was pained to see these children being subjected to the path of least resistance when it came to education. I still firmly believe that a child's mind is tempered under the fires of adversity. By challenging the students, they will begin to figure out and confront newer problems. They will even devise ways to excel when presented with an obstacle they cannot image they will ever topple, but they do so just the same. Nothing like inspiring the students to think asymmetrically as opposed to following a simple checklist. When students can utilize their own outside knowledge — instead of just restating in their own words whatever the teacher says — they will have an opportunity to really pick up problem-solving skills that will help them outside of the classroom.

Venting aside, we didn't do much for the class this week besides the students reading stories from the textbook and answering questions on their worksheets. Per usual, I was ordered to sit in the back and watch how he controls the class. From my viewpoint, it was just subjugating them to the whims of a tyrannical teacher. There was no art. There was no ease in the instruction. The students are just regurgitating the same tired information the teacher provides.

Personally, I would have them work on more profound and nuanced aspects of the story, teaching them how to really understand and deduce what is going on in a given scene or scenario, especially when analyzing a story: *If X character is presented with Y problem, within the confines of the parameters set up by the story, what are all the ways the character could solve the problem. Which one do you feel will be most effective?* I think that is way more effective than asking the students to reiterate what was happening in the story. Questions like the teacher asked required the least amount of work, the least amount of mental energy. I know humans can be cognitive misers, but students cannot excel if they lack the opportunity of turning their own mental gears, especially if the teacher does not cultivate an environment promoting such education.

For my final review for the semester, Mr. Cichy, who I would no longer refer to as Mr. Cinch, gave me an A for wasting away for 13 weeks of a boring student internship. He didn't give me any helpful feedback or anything to make me a better teacher. The sum total of his advice to assist in my future profession boiled down to how I should become familiar with a school's attendance reporting system. Considering he did not give me a chance to take attendance at any point during my internship period, I find this advice to be unhelpful. I mean, Mr. Cichy had all of the opportunity in the world to give me hands-on experience, but he decided not to. I guess if I took him up on his offer to take over his class while he just watched (and got paid), he would have given me more opportunities to grow.

Please do not let my next mentor teacher be as bad as him. I know we really need teachers, but I promise myself that these students, or any student for that matter, deserve someone better than Mr. Cichy. No wonder *THE SCHOOL DISTRICT* doesn't try to raise the school's State Letter Grade from C to A. There is no point if teachers like him are the rule rather than the exception, much to the disservice of the students and families they are supposed to be serving.

When I have my own classroom, my future mentor teacher will give me the best possibility to succeed. I know I will daily lesson plan with their guidance. I know I will only come in during the second semester, and everything is already planned ahead, but I will have the opportunity to plan side-by-side with my mentor teacher, gaining a view of what they think while preparing for the next day. I guess it should be pretty easy sailing since I will not have to create everything from scratch.

Memory before the Arizona Teachers Academy

After I woke up from the coma, I was transported from the hospital in the back of an ambulance during rush hour traffic. Even though I almost died in a car accident caused by a reckless driver, I watched in abject horror while strapped to a gurney as motorists were having a complete disregard for safety while driving in broad daylight. These fuckers had the same disregard for safety as the fucking red light runner. Cars were cutting each other off while other impatient motorists took turns riding up the ass of my ambulance. I was scared shitless. The powerlessness was solidifying within the very ambulance that was attempting to safely transport me to Maricopa Medical Center for rehabilitation. Thankfully, I made it to the hospital without incident…

I was unloaded from my ambulance, taken to my room, and I was forced to wait patiently for staff to come in and make sure I was in good spirits. I guess my survival from a brain injury was a big deal. Or maybe they didn't want me to fall out of bed when I tried to get up to go to the bathroom or walk around the hospital room.

Because the nurses at the treating hospital cut off my shirt, my pants, my underwear, and destroyed my only pair of shoes, I was pretty much left with only clothes that Mom could find at my apartment I was sharing with my roommates. Unfortunately, I was left shoeless because I did not have an extra pair of shoes. In addition, because I couldn't do all of my vocational rehab services inside the hospital, part of my care was to walk outside of the hospital to see my overall mobility post-TBI. Therefore, shoes would need to be located for me to participate and complete the activity.

My parents didn't have any money to buy me shoes, and I did not have any access to my own money (because I just woke up from a fucking coma). I also didn't have an extra pair of shoes just lying around in my apartment because even working third shift didn't afford luxuries like having extra shoes at my disposal. So, when it came to my own footwear, I would use the same pair of shoes as long as I could, and I would only think about upgrading when the sole started falling off the shoe, the back of the heel was beginning to tear, or any other shoe ailment that would force me to upgrade. This was my reward for not having the money to go to college like the rest of my friends.

Since I wasn't in the completely-able-to-process-what-was-going-on frame of mind, the technicians at the hospital had to find me something to complete the test. So, I was stuck wearing leftover shoes that the facility had on hand. Unfortunately for me, the only available shoes that could fit my feet were flat sole dress shoes. Once I got those shoes on, I was finally able to complete the activity hospital's rehabilitation specialist had in mind.

The technician, a young women around 18 years old, took me on the walk of the hospital, making sure I had the proper gait or at least was walking well enough to be functional when I was discharged.

The coup de grâce of the entire physical therapy was for me to walk outside of the hospital. By participating in this little stroll around the front of the hospital, I was supposed to walk through loose rocks while only wearing the infernal dress shoes. In the infinite wisdom of the rehab technician who worked for the Maricopa County Medical Center, they thought that was an excellent idea. I, however, had to be convinced to take that treacherous journey, being very cautious and in an almost childlike state for months after waking up from my coma.

Outside of the hospital, the Sun was extremely bright, but the first sense of scorching heat was months away; so, I believe a good description of the environment was *a pleasant morning for a regular, leisurely walk.*

The moat of rocks surrounded the facility where I was being housed. I guess this was easier and cheaper to maintain than having grass. Also, the landscaping would prevent the hospital from wasting water. That is always a good thing in a desert.

Like some kind of sick, twisted obstacle course, my task was to walk upon the loose rocks to a post about 40 yards away, walk around the post, and then walk back. I wasn't really reluctant to do this. On the contrary, I was antsy to go around, walk around, and test my abilities ever since I woke up in the hospital.

I take the first uneasy step.

No problem.

Second step.

No problem.

As I take each and every step, I grow more and more confident in my ability to navigate the terrain. I will myself into taking each step, less and less carefully, quickly increasing speed as my feeling the confidence overflows.

I walk around the post—no problem!

I am on the straightaway to the sidewalk and freedom. Nothing will stop me now. I feel confidence runneth over with every step forward, progressing past my injury, past the tinge in my right side, reminding me of my still healing ribs. The very scar tissue caused by the internal injuries from my broken ribs choking out oxygen, causing the pain to blossom, grow into a reminder of what happened to me.

10 steps.

9 steps.

8 steps.

7 steps.

6 steps.

5 steps.

4 steps.

3 steps.

2 steps.
1 step.
Last step!
Crash!

I slipped as I was stepping down. As I fell, the instinctive part of me that would have thrown out my hands in an attempt to catch myself on my downward descent was out on a lunch break or maybe grabbing a cup of coffee. So, the full force of gravity meeting hard ground became a quick reminder of why people shouldn't cross loose gravel with flat shoes. Half of my body landed in the rocks, and the other half—and my face—slammed into the sidewalk. My head bounced off the walkway.

The rough and pointy stones, hard pressed against my cheek, were the signal to move after the impact flash dissipated from my view. The taste of copper in my mouth, on my tongue. Pressing my hands, balancing to pull myself up, I stumbled to my feet. Discomfort's crescendo motivated me to check my face, my sensitive shoulder, where I find blood running down from a busted lip. The skin on my right shoulder was scraped away. The flesh torn asunder, with freckles of blood seeped through and mesmerized me.

I didn't scream.
I didn't shout.

"Are you alright?" asked the physical therapist.

I nodded, still in a daze from bouncing off the sidewalk.

"We'll call it a day. Let me help you back to your room."

The physical therapist interlocked her left and right arms around my arms as if we walked down the aisle to some hospital wedding.

The abrupt end of my PT session for the day taught me two valuable things. First, I will never wear flat sole shoes when walking across loose rocks or gravel (even if a physical therapist suggests I do it). Second, I will instinctively throw out my hands to catch myself if I feel myself begin to slip. It sucked that I needed to learn both lessons the hard way. On the bright side, I did get to go to my room, and the physical therapist came back later with some ice cream and painkillers. So, I relaxed, watched TV, and returned to the routine day-to-day procedures of being in a hospital with nothing better to do.

January 18th, 2019

On Friday of last week, I received an email for my Spring Semester student teaching assignment from Mr. James Saille, my clinical coordinator. The email just filled me in with usual formalities like the school district, the Phoenix School District (PSD), location, Michael Joseph Mansfield High School (MJMHS), the classroom assignment, 9th Grade English with Mr. Peter Sona, and what time I needed to show up every day, 7:30 AM because classes start at 7:55.

As I walked towards MJMHS, I noticed, admired how this is was such a newer building than the previous school. Overall, I think the layout of the school reminds me of my old high school. It is one massive, three-story building. The exterior is very intimidating, foreboding (especially for students who did not do their homework). Imagining how news students would walk up and get intimidated by the structure, I felt a shiver go down my spine.

As I was navigating towards Mr. Sona's class, I walked across the grass space in front of the school, entering through the exterior double doors. I was greeted by campus security after entering the building. I am forced to empty my pockets into a bin, a bin that goes through a conveyor belt with an x-ray machine while the stationed security guard does a quick inspection of the contents. I also had to walk through the corresponding metal detectors, receive a quick look-over while I held my hands up and displayed my University ID. It reminds me of security for an airport.

With the security theater completed, I walked past both offices for administration and the nurse on the right while the library's entrance was left. After the library and the offices, the left and right paths branch off from the central pathway, leading to two other hallways and more classrooms.

As I walked down the hallway, I memorized the layout of the interior. Each floor has three corridors. The left, right, and middle. There are stairs at six points along the outer walls: the southwest, the west, the northwest, the northeast, the east, and the southwest sections of the building, and elevators at the southwest, southeast, northeast, and northwest for students who are unable to take the stairs. Along each side of a corridor/hallway, there are three doors on each side for a total of six classrooms per corridor. In addition, each floor has one teacher's lounge in the middle of the central hall, leaving 17 classrooms per floor. With 17 classrooms per floor and three levels, the school has about 51 instructional spaces within the school building. Since the gym and other extracurricular classes are outside the main building, the school was one of the largest ones I have ever seen.

Mr. Sona's class is one of the closer classrooms near the teachers' lounge on the first-level corridor. My mentor teacher's classroom felt very spacious, allowing even more students to come and go. Unlike LIHS and its cramped, rundown feeling, I think the District put more money into this location. I guess they are trying to attract the wealthier students from the nearby communities, bringing their donor families with them. This should be a pretty fun, easygoing experience.

For Mr. Sona himself, he has reddish hair, a small mustache with hints of blond, broad shoulders, and a gut that hang over his belt. His looks and how he carries himself reminds me of St. Nick, only if St. Nick decided to forgo the white hair for red and shaved his beard. Mr. Sona even has the constant smile and the red face down pat.

For my first evaluation for the week, Mr. Sona complimented me on how I was an expert on the subject we were teaching (English). Also, I have familiarity with using proximity — how close I stand near students to make sure they stay task — to help keep students on task while also minimizing disruptions. Because I believe students should respect me, recognize me as an authority figure, I strongly feel managing student behavior this semester will not be an issue. Also, I am glad that I am allowed to take attendance without begging the teacher to let me do my job (finally). Thankfully. I may be able to catch up on the lost progress from the previous semester.

I still need to get the pronunciation right for all 126 students across five classes in Mr. Sona's schedule. To make my life a whole lot easier, I will copy what I saw online and create a seating chart to practice a student seat location while also working on their individual names (that I spelled phonetically). I will help myself out by asking each student how to say their name correctly so it will be easier to document.

To help draw a better connection with the students, I will ask them to share a small story or their favorite food as examples of distinguishing characteristic that makes it easier for me to remember them. One of my professors stated that if I fail to remember student names, I'll delay any opportunity to build a long-lasting trust that will last for the whole year. This will also help prevent me from completely disregarding their individuality. I want them to have the utmost trust and me and view me as someone who has a vested interest in their individual performance. I do not want them to view me as someone who doesn't care (or who can care less like other teachers I know), causing me to take my rightful place as just another outsider and not someone trying to make a difference.

The importance of names, of identity were hammered into me by my education classes at the community college and in graduate school. How can a teacher have authority if they are unable to remember a student's name? A simple mispronunciation may be funny the first few times, but repeatedly mispronouncing a student's name will kill any leverage I may have over the student, a student who'll instantly view me as someone who doesn't really care about them. Behavioral problems will be retaliation for carelessness and a complete disregard of student autonomy.

When developing an activity, Mr. Sona allowed me to use a few students he selected to help with their English acquisition. So, I am going to utilize an independent/dependent clause and complex sentence refresher activity. I think this will help the students overall by reintroducing more ways for their brains to code in information. I honestly believe that providing students more avenues to internalize information will drastically improve their overall writing ability. By being better writers, I think the students will become better thinkers.

The overall activity was 40 questions tasking the students to identify and label the independent and dependent clauses of 10 sentences. After this activity, the students write in 10 dependent clauses that match the independent clause provided. Next, the students would create 10 complex sentences by creating an independent clause for the dependent clause I supplied. The final section would assess their ability to create complex sentences with independent and dependent clauses in response to a prompt regarding the literature they are currently reading.

From the way the students processed the information and how they scored 100% on the formative assessment, I really believe the students picked a tool they will use in the future. If they do not, I will be really disappointed. So, next week, I will reinforce this week's lesson by checking on the students' work, making sure they retain the information. I may even give them a little pop quiz to see if they can still supply the correct answers to the question prompts like fill in the blank, providing questions requiring complex sentences to fully answer the question.

I know the students may not remember all of this, so I may need to review the activity to make sure the students write in a way that fulfills the state requirements. The ability to convey wants and desires is a vital tool the students can use moving forward. Because rhetoric is an art these students will use for the rest of their lives, they will need to utilize it as quickly as possible. Beyond my class, suppose the students want to convince a teacher they deserve a particular grade. In that case, students appear more ethical if they can artistically persuade the teacher why an A+ is the only appropriate grade for the assignment, the quarter, or even the semester.

Memory before the Arizona Teachers Academy

Awaken by a sudden ring, I slowly reached over to the cell phone lying on the floor next to my bed. I thought to myself: *Today is Labor Day. Who the fuck is calling me at 7 am on a holiday?*

"Hello?"

"Mom is dead."

"What?"

"While I was in the shower this morning, Mom was on the bed. I heard her call out to me asking for me to come because she needed help, but when I answered back, she just responded with 'never mind; so, I went back to the shower. When I came out, she was on the bed, and I couldn't wake her up. She wasn't breathing. So, I called over the friend from next door to try to revive her. He's an EMT. We both did everything we could, but she didn't wake up. So, you really need to come over here quickly because you should see her before the funeral home takes her away."

I quickly got out of bed, threw on whatever I could wear, I jumped into my car, and took off. I was racing down the surface streets. I didn't care who was in the way because I wanted to make sure my mom was alright. I wanted to see her. I wanted to make sure my Dad wasn't playing some cruel joke on me. I love my mom so much, and I didn't know what to do.

When I got on the freeway, I was doing what was likely 105 MPH in my little hybrid car. This would have been a perfect opportunity for me to get pulled over for reckless driving, but I guess it was too early on Labor Day to see any cops out. I passed all 10 exits in what felt like way too long. It felt like hours, even though it shouldn't have taken that long at the rate I was traveling.

Why would Dad lie to me?

My 30th birthday is only in two days.

92

Is he telling the truth?

Is he pranking me because I ignore Mom too much?

What was the last thing I said to Mom?

Did Dad play this trick on me because she called me at the same time yesterday?

But I was born on Labor Day.

Did I tell her I loved her yesterday?

This has to be a joke.

Dad likes joking with me when I don't give Mom enough time.

Every motion, every turn, I was on autopilot. I was there, I was present, but I also wasn't. I couldn't focus. My father's words were still resonating within me. She shouldn't be gone. She couldn't be gone. She was only 51-years-old. What am I going to do? If she is really gone, I already miss her so much. I started thinking about what was the last things I said to her. Replaying every conversation over in my mind, hoping to rationalize the way I interacted with her.

I know some people lose touch with their parents because of rampant mistreatment. In my case, it was something more benign. It was caring too much, being fixated too much on how I was doing. After all, I was her firstborn. This egotistical belief is based solely on observing and remembering how she treated me and how she treated Taylor. I know Taylor was a good sibling, but I could not ignore how we were treated differently. Even though Taylor was younger, I was Mom's favorite. When children feel their parents have a favorite, I believe it eventually causes a fissure to form between the siblings. For us, our specific chasm formed during our middle-school years, and it grew even larger while we were in high school.

Because she was loved me too much, I would likely try to rush her off the phone, so I could get peace from work, but she would always call me a few minutes later, forgetting that she had already called and talked to me. I blame her prescriptions for her incessant calling.

I remember she called me on Sunday (yesterday). Because of how her prescriptions affected her perception of time and her repeated times of calling me early in the morning, I forgave myself for getting off the phone with her so quickly. I was tired. I feel I was staying up too late playing video games or doing some mundane task, like surfing the internet or baking some cookies, is what I told myself to rationalize getting her off the phone quickly. If only I was willing to listen to her, ready to talk to her, I would give up everything just to speak with her one more time.

But I can't.

If what my Dad said is true, I will never get to talk to her again. I will never get to tell her how my day was, what I was doing in my life. I would not ever get a moment like that with her again. Her answer would only be silence since she would no longer be there, gone. Forever.

"*I will call you back later*" was the last words I ever uttered to her. Did I tell her I loved her? How long was she waiting for a phone call that never came? If I only knew she would never talk to me again, and I would never see her again, I know I would have never hung up that phone. I would have spoken to my mom…forever. I really wish I could take it back, call her back, but I can't because she will not be there to listen. Who she was dissipated from this Earth with her dying breath two days before my 30th birthday.

While I was lost in my own rationalization and self-loathing, I instinctively made the Peoria Avenue exit. Sometimes it frightens me what I can do when I am on autopilot. I need to stop. I need to focus on the road. But, unfortunately, my mind wanders too much. Even if I drive somewhat safely when I am on *autopilot*, I am incredibly reckless and can potentially harm someone or myself. But, because I have been to their house so many times, traveled the freeway on numerous occasions to get there (maybe drop off some food to them), my autopilot was no different than putting a car in cruise control when going down the freeway between Phoenix and Flagstaff or Tucson.

Even as I neared 13th Avenue, I was just rolling through all the different scenarios of ways I could have handled talking to my mom, ways I could have treated her better. I could have helped pay for her rent to move out of a house owned by a slum lord that should have been condemned instead of being for rent. The horrible house, infested with roaches and disease, should have not been her place of death. If this is a trick, if my Dad is lying to me, I will make them pack up and move out. She shouldn't be living there anymore. They need a new place, a better place for them to grow old in.

I turned the corner at 13th Avenue. Amongst houses and various apartment buildings in different states of disrepair, I saw the white van parked right in front of my parents' house. I knew my Dad was not lying: My mother was dead.

As I got out of my parked car, two gentlemen started to unload a cart to take her away. I walked to my parents' front door, my grandfather, my Mom's stepfather, walked out of the front door carrying DVDs.

"I'm just getting the movies back that your Mom borrowed," he mumbled to me. No sorry for your loss. Your Mom was a great person. Nothing. Just some throwaway line about getting movies back from a person who just started to grow cold.

I walked past my grandfather, through the cluttered front area that was treated mostly as storage then anything. There was a useless computer, a nonworking TV, some assorted furniture, crates, and boxes of all kinds. It was an obstacle course as I carefully walked into the living room

with my Dad's favorite chair right in front of the 62"
television — playing an infomercial.

I looked over at the filthy kitchen, microwave
hanging open because someone forgot to close it. The
round table had leftover a bucket of fast food chicken that
had been sitting there for God only knows how long.

I went to the back room, the master bedroom. She
was on the bed, eyes closed like she was sleeping all of
those times I came home from school. The reality was there
lying on that bed, and I could do nothing to change it. My
Dad and his friend were next to me.

"I tried everything," said the friend. "I am an EMT,
and we tried everything for twenty minutes. I'm so sorry."

January 25th, 2019

Well, this was an interesting second week of student teaching. Monday and Tuesday went well. I came into the classroom and worked more so than I had previously. Mr. Sona gave me more time to directly work with and monitor the students' progress. I wasn't allowed to teach my own lesson or anything, but I did not waste the opportunity to build relationships with the students. Because I was still new, I mostly observed and helped out when I could. He told me he decided to go slowly with me because he felt I needed more time, a more secure safety net, to ensure I was comfortable with the students. Mr. Sona said he didn't want to cause them any larger of a disruption than having someone new in his class. If I rushed into taking over his five classes, I would potentially harm my overall performance, and I would more likely give up teaching in a few years. So, I guess I was more than comfortable with this temporary setup.

On Wednesday, before the start of the school day (because it was a late start for the students), I met with Mr. Saille and Mr. Sona before school. The general topic of the meeting was to make sure I was willing and able to participate in the student teaching activity and what everything really entails. At the same time, this little conference attempted to preview the added expectations later in the semester. I was a little surprised by the decision to have the meeting before class, especially since Mr. Saille was a special education teacher at another school. So, I didn't know how he would make it to our meeting and then get to his school in time for the students. But I wasn't going to question their decision. If he wanted to miss class, I guess it was okay. I think the rationale was not to be interrupted by any students during the process because Mr.

Sona had conditioned his students not to enter the classroom before the morning bell.

During our conversation, I notified both of them of my health history, particularly my survival from a severe brain injury. I did this because I wanted to make sure they understood why I became a teacher. Remembering back to my childhood and living out of hotels, I reaffirmed my desire, my drive to tackle a profession where parents and critics of public education will treat me like dirt. I guess a good term for the justification behind going into teaching should be labeled as *survivor's guilt*. This palpable sense of not wasting an opportunity was given to me. Because I cannot switch places, cannot give up everything to help all the others suffering from being in a coma, stuck in a lowered state of consciousness, had a large portion of who they were torn away from them, or no longer have the ability to comprehend how their life is radically changed, I strive to do what they cannot.

In other words, I feel incredibly fortunate to be alive today, haunted by the memory of the woman who could not talk because of her brain injury while I was at Arizona's Premier Rehabilitation Center. With her locked into a condition I will never understand, I knew I couldn't give any less than my very best. I told my mentor teacher and my clinical coordinator I was taking this opportunity to help before I may be stuck in such a state as her. As we sat at three desks, all facing each other, I began to go into specific detail about why I wanted to become a teacher.

"Watching the news, I hear we have a national teacher shortage. So, *The School District* will welcome someone with my academic, health, and historical background to help connect the importance of education to the students' personal and financial goals. In addition, someone like me who has overcome obstacle after obstacle after obstacle to get to this point may inspire some students to work harder than they possibly could ever imagine. They will be able to shape and transform this world into something drastically different than my own teenage years. Don't you agree?"

Mr. Saille and Mr. Sona looked at each other and then looked at me.

"I thank you for sharing this with us," Mr. Saille said with compassion in his voice. "People like you can really add so much to the teaching profession. Being someone who had an IEP and a 504 Plan would really do a wonderful job connecting with those students."

"Uh," I interjected. "I didn't have an IEP or 504 plan when I attended elementary school, middle school, or high school. I was in all advanced classes. For example, when I attended high school, my AP Government class actually released a Voters' Guide for my school district…"

"Okay," nodded Mr. Sona. He appeared to be listening carefully. However, I could see the same face he showed his students when they aired their own concerns about any apparent exigency that prevented them from turning in their assignments on time.

"So," I said with the confidence of having someone listen to my ideas earnestly, "I would want to do something like that with the families in the neighborhood. I would want to work with the government teacher and get the 11th Graders or 12th Graders an opportunity to work on something like that down here. It would be an excellent addition to their portfolios."

"That sounds like a good idea." Mr. Sona appeared to be in agreement. "Unfortunately, I don't think it would work down here. Most of the families do not like to get involved with politics. They just send their kids to school, and that is it. So, I like the idea, but you may want to save that for another opportunity at another school in the future."

"Oh. Thank you for letting me know. I wouldn't want to let anyone down or cause any problems."

"Sharing your ideas," Mr. Saille interjected, "is nothing you should feel down about. However, if you have ideas like that in the future, you may want to share them with your department lead. They will offer you a lot of help putting any of your ideas into action, okay?"

"Yeah, I don't want to cause any problems as well. But, I really wanna finish this up and get my own classroom, ya know?"

Overall, I think it was a nice little meeting, and I don't think it could go any better. I just need to make sure that I am prepared for the coming weeks. Mr. Sona said that I would be taking over class periods once or twice a week pretty soon. I am almost there. It is only a few weeks from my grasp.

On Thursday, I had my first observation, even though I hadn't really had any chance to teach Mr. Sona's class. I guess now was as good of time as any. I mainly received twos and a couple threes. It was early, and I still need to gain an understanding of how to adequately do well managing a class. Since it was only the first time Mr. Saille rated me on my classroom performance, and very few students pass their student teaching on their first observation, I mentally comforted myself with my two other chances of being judged by Mr. Saille. The fourth observation is just where the student teacher signs off on all of the forms, and everyone calls it a semester since it is the last day of the student teaching experience.

So, for each observation, the clinical coordinator is instructed to grade using the Teaching Skills, Knowledge and Responsibilities Performance Standards, otherwise known as the TAP Rubric. The TAP Rubric is a system utilizing a five-point scale where 1 was failing, 3 was average, and 5 was excelling. To pass the student teaching assignment, I would need to receive at least a three from Mr. Saille before the end of the semester. Typically, it should have three observations. If a student needs additional opportunities, the fourth meeting will become a fourth observation and the last time a student teacher has a chance of passing the class. Even though it is supposed to be systematic and objective, the majority of the measurements are measured subjectively by the clinical coordinator.

This means I will have about two more observations to earn my threes. This appears to be as easy as pie. I just need to do the work, and I will make sure my mentor teacher actually works with me.

Memory before the Arizona Teachers Academy

The burst of the housing market and the subsequent Great Recession provided me the opportunity to finally buy a house of my very own, escaping from my confinement to apartment living. Even though it was harmful for millions of families, I was fortunate enough to have the money at the right time. There is a lot of talk of people buying a house from a distressed owner and then turning it into a rental property. I could never take advantage of a poor individual forced give up their chance at the American Dream. I wasn't such a person. I have a conscious, and I like to look myself in the mirror without wincing. I just found a home that would satisfy the needs of me and my future family.

Before finding the home of my dreams on some website, I went to several homes in foreclosure or houses owned by individuals who were trying to short sell. I would send over the MLS (multiple listing service) numbers to our agent. We would then check out the house, find something that would cause us to change our mind, and continue to look. We looked, and looked, and couldn't find anything. But I eventually hit the jackpot.

I was pretty damn lucky to find a house that was near a nature preserve. The white walls and brown roof didn't really differ from any of the other potential properties in the area, but it did have a nice 15-foot saguaro in the front yard. The house was bank-owned, meaning the house would come "as-is" and wouldn't do any kind of repairs. I was comfortable with the home purchase because the previous "owner" was likely a home flipper, and they bought the house before the bottom fell out of the market. The bank foreclosed on the property and I got a hefty discount in the process. It was also priced incredibly low. Me being completely unfamiliar with the housing process, I paid for an inspection of the house, but I did not really heed any of the potential problems. I was hyper-focused on just buying the home and starting a new chapter in my life, having to share my walls with some stranger.

Now, the original owners who sold to the home-flippers appeared must have been an elderly couple. I could tell because there was a bar to help a person balance as they tried to sit down in the master bathroom. I imagined what they would feel like living in their house. I hoped their happiness would provide my family the same level of contentment as them.

But as I said, I didn't do a proper inspection on the house…

Almost six months after I had moved into the house, the first monsoon storm of the season was incredibly nasty to all except the most seasoned Phoenicians. Because of the way the community was developed, all of the water flowed down towards 41st Avenue. I didn't have a car at the time, so I was basically stuck home throughout the entire storm. Torrents of water came flowing from my roof, raindrops smashing into my bedroom window; the 15-foot saguaro on the little hill right in front of my window was being pulled by the wind. Back and forth. Back and forth. An event like this would concern newbies to Arizona, but I have lived here for almost three decades. For me, it was a lullaby. For me, it reminded me of my childhood Florida home years ago. With this lullaby, I fell asleep with the smacking sound of high winds and pouring rain.

The following morning, I got up. I exited the guestroom and struggled to get ready for the day. Even though the master bedroom was more enormous than the other three guest rooms and had a connected walk-in closet, the built-in shelf in the shower had a significant dip and was separated from the polarized window seal in the shower (allowed natural light to flow into the entire master bath). Whatever was holding up the shelf could be caused by several potential reasons: there may have been a flaw in the design, termites may have eaten away whatever braced the entire structure, or maybe it was pushed down by the bodyweight of someone who decided to sit up there.

So, I felt the bathroom was completely unusable until I decided to repair that section of the walk-in shower because I did not want to risk any water draining into the space between the shelf and the window and potentially increasing damage to the house or introduce moisture for black mold to grow. I could only imagine what the outside of the house looked like during those few times I showered in the master bathroom. Did the shower water drain outside of the wall if I ever decided to take a shower? Was the water further damaging the house's foundations? How much money would it cost me to repair this *little* problem?

With the significant problem with the master bathroom, I decided upon the path of least resistance and allowed myself a small comfort by just sleeping in one of the guestrooms. I did not have the money to spend on the shower repair at that moment, but I forgave myself for not going out to fix such a little problem because this house was bigger than any apartment I lived in at any point in my life. It also gave me the chance to have a peaceful night's sleep because local parties wouldn't wake me up at odd hours of the night.

So, I walked over to the hallway bathroom. I did my usual preparation for the day. I used the bathroom, showered, and brushed my teeth. I went back to my bedroom, got dressed, and decided to make breakfast. Everything went the way it was supposed to happen. Just a typical, uneventful morning.

My front doorbell rang.

I opened the front door.

Through the screen door I answered, "Hello?"

"Hey," my neighbor answered. "Your cactus fell down, and it's in the middle of the street."

"What?" I answered while as I quickly opened the front door.

"Yeah, it looks like it fell down during the storm."

As I walked behind the neighbor, I noticed how the saguaro was now gone. The mighty giant had fallen. Because the cactus fell away from my house, my eyes could now really understand and appreciate the size of my former, spiny guardian. It no longer towered over me, over my home. The cactus was sprawled across the front of my yard, the sidewalk, and about 1/3rd of the street in front. It was mostly intact except for the cracks at the bottom from hitting the ground.

If the wind was blowing in the other direction, I don't know if my house would have stopped the saguaro from crashing into me while I slept. I began to imagine what it would have been like to have the cactus slam through my window and ruin my evening. I guess I could count myself fortunate. Instead of bringing a cool refreshing drink, the behemoth would have given me an abrupt, early exit from this stage.

The neighbor and I had a little laugh about how lady luck was and wasn't on my side last night. Even though I was still alive, I would need to pay for the removal. I hoped there was someone who offered cheap removal of an uprooted saguaro.

While I was still outside, I pulled out my phone and researched to see for saguaro removal. Unsurprisingly, everything I was finding was either too far away, or the company would charge an exorbitant fee. It was very disconcerting, especially since the HOA would slap me with a hefty fine for having a downed saguaro in the street, bringing down the home values of everyone else in the neighborhood, even the super large mansion with the giant gate along 41st Avenue.

As I reflected on the dire situation, a landscaping company pulled around the corner and stopped by a neighbor who lived further down the street. I hoped they would be able to remove the minor problem for me. I guess I was lucky they showed up when they did because they could remove the cactus for about $100 cash. So, this little storm was not as bad as it could have been with all things considered.

February 1st, 2019

Well, I just concluded my third week of student teaching. Sadly, I am still not allowed to do the weekly lesson plans with Mr. Sona. He always likes to plan the day before, which I find a bit odd because I am in his classroom. One of the requirements to host a student teacher was to turn over all their available material, allowing the student teacher to plan for each week. Because Mr. Sona was unwilling to provide me the information, my lesson plans were always late.

Unfortunately for me, I was told by Mr. Saille that it didn't matter how much work my mentor teacher did or if they even followed a lesson plan that I developed. The only thing that really mattered was for me to just do it. This didn't make sense to me. If I am supposed to be learning by emulating my mentor teacher, and the mentor teacher is supposed to be guiding me, why am I learning now that teachers kind of wing it the day before? They spend about 30 minutes slightly changing a presentation provided to them by the instructional lead teacher with information from the students and calling it a day.

I guess this really surprised me when I was going into my first student teaching experience. There was no weekly planning based on how students were doing. There was no adapting the material for the specific needs of students. It was just a 30-minute exercise on making a few changes and providing it to all the students of all the classes the next day. I guess Mr. Sona didn't need to do as much work when preparing for his students.

Overall, I find things to be going along very well. The students are fantastic, and Mr. Sona is pretty welcoming to everyone in his class. But, shockingly, he does say a few inappropriate things to me about students, mainly this one student who identifies as Black. Now, I think it could be an old-school mentality or maybe Mr. Sona is from another State where it is okay to view students in such a way, but I don't know. It just makes me a little uncomfortable how he thinks the student should be in a special education class because she cannot read, according to him. But, on the other hand, the student could also reflect the educational environment. Instead of helping the young adult, accommodating for whatever she needs, Mr. Sona wants to pass the buck along to someone else. This is likely not the first time this has happened to the young student, and I doubt it will be the last.

My mentor teacher's statement reminded me of the sister of a friend of mine when I was six years old. The 18-year old high school graduate's name was Josephine (Josey for short). Besides being a person of color like the student in Mr. Sona's class, Josey was also being shuffled along in the educational system. The system would not make sure Josey could read, only she attended school for 13 years and getting the most out of those 13 years of funding tied to the unfortunate student. If Josey and fellow students like them stayed longer than those than the allotted time — for whatever reason, the school would start running a deficit, so they would either cycle the kids out with graduation or remove them with a zero-tolerance policy for anything.

I didn't know at the time, didn't question it, but now I can see the ramifications of why students are being shuffled along to make way for other customers. Considering the state only pays for students until they are 18-years old, this *School District* would rather inflate their numbers with graduates instead of a higher student dropout rate by forcing students out who are not ready, who the education system failed.

What does this mean? Well, the teachers will adapt their instruction to create the right amount of resistance to promote student attendance, hoping they will continue showing up through the entire school year, working as much as they can until the school no longer receives funding from the state to educate the students. If the student learns something, that is a bonus. If they do not, that is just a problem caused by someone else (parents, politicians, or whatever).

I knew his students were from a lower socioeconomic class, but I did not realize that less was expected from them because of where they came from. I am becoming a teacher to combat this, and I am constantly losing hope because not much is expected of the students. I know the school's principal asked us to do more to get the students involved, hoping to raise test scores.

So, I sent off an email to the principal, carbon copying Mr. Sona in the process. I explained how my high school had a voter's guide, or how I worked on a few college literary magazines, and how WGBH Boston came down to film my AP Government class when I was in 12th Grade. I attempted to persuade the principal and Mr. Sona on the benefits of using project-based learning like creating a schoolwide literary magazine to get Mr. Sona's English classes more involved, providing the students an additional opportunity of picking up essential skills like writing and editing. This would help the students out, allowing them to buy-in, and raise test scores in the process. I really saw the benefit of giving the students more variety in acquiring the skills necessary to succeed once they were done with high school.

The idea was instantly shot down. I wasn't told why, but it didn't matter. The principal did not feel comfortable having that discussion with me, referring me back to Mr. Sona. My mentor teacher just brushed my ideas off with a callousness that was both surprising and shocking.

"You shouldn't concern yourself with planning for helping out the community or anything else. Your job is not trying to help my students at my school. You should just focus on passing your student teaching." Mr. Sona said dryly.

"Okay. Is there anything else I can do to help out? I feel kind of useless. But, because this is one of the highest-paying districts in Arizona, I really want to stand out."

"You shouldn't really worry yourself about standing out. Most of the teachers who start out here have been teachers for at least 10 years."

"Two of the people who were in my community college education program still work for the district."

"How do you know?"

"I've seen their stuff on social media."

"Okay. You shouldn't worry about any of that stuff. Just focus on passing your student teaching. Any and all of your ideas about improving a school should be saved when you get your own contract. Okay?"

"K. Uh, when are you going to lesson plan and do all of that stuff?"

"Don't worry about it."

That pretty much put an end to that conversation. Besides that little interaction that amounted to me being coached about my responsibilities as a student teacher, everything else went well overall. I was thankful that he gave me positive reviews on my knowledge of the English language. I am glad that I can quickly work within the subject because of my background in communication and rhetoric. Both subjects provide additional tools for me to utilize with the students, giving them more skills and resources to use when they move on in their academic careers.

Besides providing coaching to students on the subject, I am making positive steps to build rapport with the entire class. As I went through the program, I remember the professors ensuring everyone in the Arizona Teachers Academy understood the importance of establishing positive relationships with the students. Even though it was not stated at the time, I now realize teachers must promote student attendance at all costs. Being a counselor, an educator, and an "in loco parentis" ("in place of the parent") is the only practical way for us to continue to receive school funding from the state. If the students do not feel welcome, or their contributions within a class are not valued, they will stay home, and the state will keep the money.

No one wins, especially the teachers. Part of the job is basic customer service work. The teacher really needs to sell the education production for the consumer (the students). If the students don't value what we are teaching, they are more likely to skip the day or even the class, which means the school loses money. So I guess I will need to make sure the students really look forward to coming to my class. My job may depend on it.

So, I will continue to look up some pop culture references and entertainment news to stay abreast of the changing trends. My job will depend on it, but it shouldn't be a laborious process because the information is readily available. I just need to peruse social media to see what is trending. I like to use my smartphone anyway, so I will spend extra time providing additional background details to help the students.

Memory before the Arizona Teachers Academy

Even though it was only about four months post-accident, I still lacked the authorization to return to work. I found it comforting that the company provided me short-term disability that paid only about 80% of my regular pay, but if I my short-term disability only went six months, my job would be waiting for me when I was medically cleared to return to my job. If it took longer than six months, I would be placed on long-term disability, receive only about 50% of my wages and my job would be gone.

Because of lack of money and lack of anywhere to go, I was limited to either staying at home or going to rehab after my accident. Even as a hardcore gamer who spent time doing game reviews for different websites, I found gaming to be entertaining when it was nothing more than a hobby, not the be-all end-all of my day-to-day existence. The entire exercise grew monotonous after my first week just sitting on my ass and playing games. I guess I found the journey to rehabilitation as a welcome break from staying at home.

Before receiving medical clearance to return to work full-time, I needed to speak with a neuropsychologist once a week to document and track my emotional/neurological recovery during my physical therapy. The sessions always boiled down to a set of discussions about how I have handled the change and what disruptions to my life occurred to me post-accident. Because I was not unaware nor incoherent like other patients being treated at this facility, the doctor and I would always discuss the state of the world.

The first week was basically just me introducing myself and having a friendly chat with the doctor. The typical little discussion allowed the neuropsychologist to gauge my encoding and decoding skills during an ordinary conversation. It was just an initial view to see if I had any significant deficits. Nothing too horrible.

During the second weekly session, my neuropsychologist commented on how well I was doing. As part of my therapy, the doctor recommended that I read a book about Phineas Gage. I had never heard of this gentleman before and my curiosity switched to full throttle because it was a story tangentially related to me. So, I asked her what the name of the book was. It was a somewhat wordy title penned by a world-renowned neuroscientist: the 1994 book called *Descartes' Error: Emotion, Reason, and the Human Brain* by Dr. Antonio Damasio. The book chronicled the story of neuroscientist's treatment of a patient who developed a brain tumor, a tumor that severely impaired his quality of life. This was compared to Phineas Gage, a railroad foreman who suffered a penetrating brain injury while leveling the ground for a railroad track on September 13th, 1848. When explosives accidentally detonated, the famous brain injury survivor's face and brain were impaled by iron rod, severely damaging his left frontal lobe in the process. Like Dr. Damasio's patient, Mr. Gage suffered a drastic change to his personality post-injury.

Apparently, Dr. Damasio's patient, Phineas Gage, and I both shared similar left-frontal lobe injuries. Like Gage and the patient, I made a seemly quick recovery from a TBI. I guess that was something, but I don't think my injury was caused by a railroad spike piercing my head nor a tumor destroying a part of my left frontal lobe.

Based on the doctor's recommendation, I hopped on the city bus and traveled all the way down to the Cholla Branch of the Phoenix Public Library. I was fortunate enough they had a copy of the book, and I finally checked it out. I took the book back to my apartment. I got in a pair of comfortable pajamas, and I start to read the book. I fervently read every detail about Dr. Damasio's patient, hanging on to every word of how the patient's life drastically changed once he began to develop a tumor. The patient left his wife for another woman, got fired from his job, and the other women left him the second all of his money was gone. The patient was able to afford Dr. Damasio because of some Californian needs-based program. A very sobering story indeed. But the entire the patient's experiences were contrasted with Mr. Gage.

The story then intersects with what happened to the famous TBI survivor. Solemnly, I am carefully absorbed, internalized every word about how a railroad spike caused a penetrating head wound. But, surprisingly to my uninformed self, the story then abruptly ends with Gage dying at the young age of 36 years — apparently from status epilepticus (a seizure that lasts so long that the person dies due to a lack of oxygen).

He just dies like that?
He just drop dead out of nowhere?
Is that going to happen to me?
Am I just going to drop dead?
How much time do I have left?

I continued the rest of my day with normal routine activities to guarantee I wasn't too bored, but the question burned about my own mortality, a constant hum regardless of what I did or said. Dinner's companion that night was the steady drum of *how much time...how much time...how much time...do I have?*

I dwelled on what my future held. The vague, abstract idea of what I lost because of the accident now came into crystalline focus. My life was on borrowed time, and I might not even wake up the following day. I could be minding my own business, and my proverbial lights would just shut off. I would not have anyone to seek medical attention for me, and my family will find my cold body days or even weeks later.

114

I was truly alone.

I felt the pendulum beginning to swing above my head. I began to hope whenever I fell asleep the end came while I dreamt a happy dream, thought happy thoughts. I didn't want my last thoughts so consumed by the finiteness of my own experience to truly appreciate what I even survived.

Why did I survive? Why was I spared? The thought percolated into my conscious life.

When fatigue finally overwhelmed my self-pity, the destruction of the continued rumination would provide a short-term reprieve. So, I got everything ready for bed with those questions unanswered but still they churned within my mind as I fell into a dark, uneasy sleep.

In the morning, as rays of light spilled into my room, I woke up with a new perspective. The worry from the day before was mostly lost. I guess I slept off my internal strife. Thankfully, my concern didn't require alcohol or anything else to numb the pain. The relaxing pillow was all I needed. I was still alive, and maybe I may avoid Mr. Gage's fate.

February 8th, 2019

The fourth week came and went without anything eventful. My mentor teacher is still limiting me to only one lesson a week. Talking to the other members of my cohort, I discovered most have already transitioned into teaching more than one class, three or more days a week. It appears their teachers are trusting their student teachers more with guiding and instructing a class full of students. I am, on the other hand, being held to just one day a week for God only knows what reason.

Unfortunately, the only day I am allowed to show my abilities is "Late Start" Wednesday, the shortest day of the week. I cannot comprehend why Mr. Sona is not giving me more opportunities to teach. He complimented my grasp of the English language. He even explained how the depths of English understanding can really help students who urgently need additional ELL ("English Language Learner") instruction. He even said how his school serves a large number of students who are identified as ELL.

So, what is going on?

Is this because I asked him about what he did before becoming a teacher?

Or was this about last week's conversation and my disclosure of my own health history?

When I discussed the issues with him after class on Thursday, he said he wanted to make sure his students were prepared for the upcoming State tests. If they did not perform well enough, it could cause problems on his yearly evaluation. In addition, Mr. Sona stated he needed to ace his principal's walkthrough so he could get promoted to being an assistant principal next year.

I understood the sentiment. Mr. Sona just wanted to move up within PSD to assistant principal and get a pretty hefty salary bump, but he promised I would have more opportunities to work with students, more time to teach once PSD was done with the standardized tests in April. He volunteered to have a student teacher in his classroom, so was he only using me so he could have a teacher's aide without needing to cut through any administrative red tape? I feel Mr. Sona failing to live up to his promise to program to maximize his own upward mobility places me at an increased disadvantage. He is tying me down to being nothing more than a mere spectator, stealing from me the entire student teacher experience to serve his own selfish ends. I am going to be wholly unprepared for the teacher's job market.

Is this because I disclosed my health history to him and Mr. Saille?

Is this a way to remove my ability to be competitive and gain a position at a more prestigious school?

I don't know if I should bring this up to someone in charge of student placement at *The University*. Should I say something? I mean, the mentor teacher keeps pushing back on trusting me with more responsibilities in his classroom. His rationale seems very weak, almost as bad as a student saying "the dog ate my homework." It feels like Mr. Sona's intention is to deny me the opportunity to follow the planned teacher preparation steps because he doesn't deem me as worthy. If I am not allowed to really grow, get my hands dirty in the teaching profession, he'll effectively strangle my dream of being an educator and all of this time wasted will be for nothing.

Next week, I need to be very insistent on gaining access to Mr. Sona's syllabus that he gave to all of his students at the start of the year. If I have this information, I believe I can at least correctly construct lessons for the students (hopefully he lets me teach them). This is high school and these are 9th graders, so they should cover F. Scott Fitzgerald's *The Great Gatsby* at some point.

If I am right, I need to think of activities that will help them deal with the eventual tragedy in the book. Additionally, I need to look at the state standards to plan out the appropriate skills the students should learn from this unit.

During the week, the PSD renovated all three of the teacher's lounges at MJMHS. Because of change in funding and the District believing the status of all the classrooms in this new school was atrocious, the voters would support a budget override all schools within the district. So, as a tiny gesture to the current teachers who had to wait until next summer for their classrooms to be revamped, the teachers' lounges on all three levels received renovations as a small olive branch.

The front part of the renovated lounges was just regular tile flooring, tables, copy machines, two tables, and the bathrooms. PSD motivational posters, school schedule, and other positive education posters were attached to each one of the off-white brick walls. In the center of the wall on the other side of the room, directly across from the entrance to the lounge, there was a door to the teacher relaxation center. The area was had brown walls with more school district posters. There were more tables and chairs, but the noteworthy addition was the five sleeping pods, similar to what some tech firms use to allow people to rest while on the job.

Supposedly, these were added so the classroom teachers could rest during their prep periods or if they wanted to take a nap during their lunch. Food was strictly prohibited in this room. All the teachers were excited about the new addition because no more than five teachers had the same prep period, meaning there weren't any problems for any of the teachers fitting in a bit of a nap if one was on their menu.

The administration felt if the school could not present itself as a united front (teachers being concerned about how much they were paid), the students would suffer from the ever-increasing strife between the educators and the administration. If the teachers were at odds with admin (the public face of the school), the parents would be less likely to send their kids to school, or they would pull their kids out and place them into charter schools, leaving their educational funding at home or with another company, causing a potential budget shortfall for the school and the district at large. A future of teachers being RIFed (reduction in force) would be the likely result.

But on the topic of how student teachers were being treated by their mentor teachers, Mark, a member of my cohort at another school, began to complain about the mistreatment he was receiving from his mentor teacher. Evidently, Mark begged to go back down to where he interned last semester. The former school was in a better position to treat him like a future teacher instead of just classroom help. So, Mark complained to the Clinical Supervisor and the Program Director at *The University*, and he will be moved back to his old location next week. The teacher at the old school are more than happy to help him out, if only my own internship was more positive.

I thought these Mentor teachers were supposed to help out, guide us? So what the hell is going on? Maybe it was that particular school or something. Because the school where I am stationed at is supported by an extremely active teachers union (and the backbone of the Arizona chapter of the national union), and Mark's district was not, perhaps that would explain what happened to him.

Memory before the Arizona Teachers Academy

With all of its lovely nature and arid landscape, Arizona does not foster memories of awe for those stricken by poverty. With a dad who was a high school dropout and a mom who could not hold down a job and was collecting disability payments, we had to make the best with what options we had, even if it meant having to wait for my mom's case manager to find somewhere we could live that wasn't infested by roaches or mice.

The case manager found the place for us, and it was a welcome surprise. The apartment complex on Mountain View Rd. was our first residence after leaving the hotels near David Crockett Elementary School. We lived there from the end of my 6th Grade year until the start of my 10th Grade. My Dad would help lower our rent by being a handyman. Everything was going well until we couldn't afford to pay the electric bill anymore, and our power was shut off. The apartment complex guaranteed my family that if our apartment didn't have power, the infraction would constitute a breach of our lease. So we were evicted for paying the rent but not paying the electricity.

My family was forced to relocate from the apartment complex where my Dad worked to a new duplex owned by someone who "slumlord" would be considered the highest of compliments. When a family is out of money, especially out of options, and they are in search of a place to call home, the vultures descend from their constant, circling vigil in the skies above to feast upon the decaying carcass of what should have been a typical, American family life. Unfortunately for us, the slumlord was more than able to get his fill.

The place we found was just some crumbling duplex. Extremely outdated and antiquated is using the term lightly. It looked like it was built in the 1960s because the units used two giant swamp coolers ("evaporative coolers") for each of the units.

To let the place stand out a little more, make it more welcoming, both units had their own yards. The people in the front had a small front yard, while we had a giant backyard (with a huge oak tree in the middle). Even though it was positive, and we had a typical, wooden gate in complete disrepair seal off our section of yard, a buzzkill was a complete lack of grass. Just dirt. Everywhere. This dirt would make our house extra filthy and a constant cleaning nuisance, if my family was diligent about maintaining cleanliness in such a location.

With the extra clutter and a mattress that was not exactly clean, our home became infested with all kinds of bugs. The lack of cleanliness made our home an especially perfect candidate as a breeding ground for bed bugs. Those tan and brown bastards would invade with a ferocity every piece of our furniture, the couches, and especially the beds. A ritual would occur where we would inspect the piping of the mattress in the hopes of finding and killing any of these little bastards that couldn't hide as well as their companions and allowing us to sleep without fear of waking up the next morning with bites all over our bodies.

Whenever an unlucky one was found, it would be killed on the spot, usually crushed. The eventual result was the piping near either the head or the foot of the bed would eventually become stained with the innards of dead bed bugs mixed with our blood from their feeding from the night before. The piping was eventually became the bed bugs' pox-marked graveyard.

Regardless of how much time we spent trying to save us from the scourge, everyone in the house would wake up with a few bites every day, regardless of where they slept. We couldn't afford to pay for an exterminator to spray the entire house, nor would the landlord even think about taking care of the problem. If we asked him to hire someone, he told my Dad that the cost would be permanently added to our rent, making treatment and prevention entirely out of the question.

The infestation was so bad, so severe that when my parents came to the decision to get rid of one of our couches and replace it with something newer. Instead of giving it away to some poor unlucky family, My Dad decided to burn the motherfucking couch. While the sofa burned, billows of smoke rose in the air above. All of us saw what felt like hundreds of those little fucking parasites trying to avoid being burned to death by crawling away as fast as they could in hopes of surviving and finding another victim later.

It was absolutely disgusting.

Besides the bed bug infestation, the lack of money also exposed another problem that required adaptation. Since our heating system relied on natural gas in addition to electricity, poverty robbed us of the ability to afford any way to heat water or even cook meals at home. Because we were lucky enough to have a microwave in the unit, the useless stove wasn't much of a nuisance. The hot water heater, however, was nothing more than a water storage unit. This became a very apparent problem whenever we decided to shower or bathe during the winter.

On the colder days of the year, I would try my best to hold off to showering until the late afternoon (usually after I got home from school). I would find the heat of the water rose from icy cold to slightly lukewarm (especially when the temperature was well over 100 degrees). Thanks to the laws of thermodynamics, the Sun's infrared radiation would slightly increase the warmth of the unheated water in the useless water heater. As a result, I found the water to be warm enough to be highly relaxing. However, if it was early in the morning or very late at night, the water would be extraordinarily frigid, instantly waking my tired ass up.

Thus, every shower during the winter was transformed into a polar bear plunge.

The first few seconds of an icy-cold deluge shocked the system, but my body quickly became used to the extreme cold. The years of daily showering in frigid water caused me to become exceptionally resilient to cold. A cold, cleansing shock was the only way to wash away the dirt, the grime of poverty. For some people, it is easy, but I know for a fact I'm not some people. I changed. I became a supporter of the whole "mind over matter" adage.

I became so used to the cold of unheated water that I was perfectly comfortable with not needing a jacket to keep warm during a school trip to Flagstaff for a speech and debate event. Hell, we were out walking around the hotel around 8PM on a snowy night, and I was just in jeans and an undershirt. The rest of my teammates complained about how cold it was while I was marveling how far my breath could go into the air. Oh, the things I did to rationalize my status in life.

February 15th, 2019

Even though my fifth week of student teaching was not the best, I am glad today is the day after Valentine's Day. I made a stop at a local drugstore on my way to student teaching. I scored some really great deals for half-priced candy. Peanut butter cups, chocolate bars, and all other assortments of candy were my reward. Unfortunately, these were all of the things that I could never share with my students because someone may have a peanut allergy, and I didn't have the medical training to give them an epinephrine injection nor the ability to carry one at my desk, leaving more candy for my family and me.

At the start of February, Mr. Sona covered all of the walls with red posters, shiny red hearts, and bigger white hearts with little romantic poems on them as a way to really help set the mood for the overall romance of the holiday. I think he went a little overboard for this holiday, but I think it makes sense. The students should view their classroom as a home away from home (or even a proper home if their own is less than ideal). The research suggests that students are more likely to perform at high levels if they believe their presence is valued.

The decorations, however, served an alternative purpose. Because we were starting to read *The Great Gatsby* this week, the classroom teacher really wants the students to understand the emotional intensity and how sex utilized as an extension of power within the context of the book. If the students did not really understand why love could be so strong, especially given the age of the characters, the students might not be able to understand what really caused the destruction of everything Gatsby held dear at the end of the book. Nevertheless, I guess setting the stage for the entire week is an excellent point.

Since research suggests some students are more visual learners, I believe this was Mr. Sona's attempt to differentiate the instruction for the students who needed it.

Throughout the week, my mentor teacher weakly attempted lesson planning with me. However, I quickly discovered Mr. Sona's lesson planning schedule was not very conducive to the program's requirements. For example, the program requires me to submit my lesson plans before the start of the week, but Mr. Sona would only plan the day before, meaning my submission for the week was almost always a week late. Also, because of Mr. Sona's conduct and inaction, the entire phone conversation with Mr. Saille, my Clinical Coordinator, was incredibly frustrating and unhelpful.

As I called Mr. Saille to please my case, hoping something could be done to alleviate the situation, I made my plea concise as a way to get to the fucking point: "how am I supposed to lesson plan for the week if Mr. Sona will not help me?" My words lacked anger, only showing a hint of desperation due to being hamstrung and hobbling towards the end of another fruitless teacher experience. If I could not lesson plan, I would be improperly trained. If the idea was to shuffle me out of the teaching profession as quickly as possible, even though the state funded my education as a way to circumvent the ongoing teacher shortage, my words and emotion convened the immediate need of a proper student teacher-and-mentor-teacher dynamic. *The University* did not assign me to Mr. Sona's class just to give him an additional state-funded teacher's aide.

"You went through the program, right?" Mr. Saille asked with a stark indifference that was both cold and unsettling. I thought the coordinator's job was supposed to be more supportive of their student teachers throughout their entire student teaching experience. I know Mr. Saille also works for *The School District*, but my position was based on the very program brochure provided to all teacher candidates who are earning a bachelor's or master's degree in education from *The University's* program, a program developed to receive the Arizona Teachers Academy state-funding. This brochure was something likely seen and signed by all educators to be allowed to have a student teacher. I mean, my mentor teacher was required to give me the materials and opportunity for successful completion of the program.

"Yeah, but...but...but I thought my mentor teacher was supposed to provide me more support. Ya know? Like lesson plan with me or give me a syllabus so I can lesson plan for myself?" My words, a mixture of raw emotion and terror of a potential failure, hung in the air. The words were not simply dancing within the ether or vanishing without a trace; they were an example of how I was not receiving the promised experience, the promised assistance to become an educator.

"I understand your concern. So, as an accommodation, both Mr. Sona and I believe giving you more time to lesson plan is important."

"Accommodation? What do you mean accommodation?" I shot back.

"Because you told us about your injured brain, correct?"

"I didn't ask for an accommodation," my concerns began to become the bedrock of this conversation. "If I was having trouble, wouldn't I have brought 'em up?"

"We thought it would be in your best interest for us to adapt your plan for you. It doesn't mean you will be learning any less than the rest of your cohort. It will just be slower. We want to make sure you really understand the material. We wouldn't want you to fall too far behind."

"I am not having any trouble. I'm good. I didn't ask—"

Cutting me off, "we thought it would be in the best interest of the overall program. The state is paying money for you to go to school, to become a teacher. You should consider yourself fortunate."

"Why?"

"We are slowing things down so you can have more time to finish the applied project."

"With everyone else is doing both at the same time, why can't I?"

"Again, I talked to the representatives from the program at *The University*, and we all believed it was in the best interest of the program for a person like you to take your time. Really learn the material."

"A person like me? I graduated with two degrees, and I finished summa cum laude. I think I am skilled enough to tackle this placement. I think I am as skilled as everyone else."

"It is nice that you finished with both your degrees with high grades, but this is not the classroom anymore. We don't know if you can really do the job. People like you should be gracious we are giving you more time. It is only to help make sure you can get a job after the program is done. So, I recommend you don't say anything else and just work with Mr. Sona as best you can for the remainder of the semester."

Memory before the Arizona Teachers Academy

Whenever I had to go to the hospital, for any reason, I felt a tinge of apprehension and worry creep over me. Why did I worry so much? Hospitals were a place for healing people, right? Was there even a reason for me to worry? No sane person would have any concern about going to the hospital to be treated. My aversion was likely based on the negative events that occurred to my family while I was still just a young child.

I mean, I cannot think of someone who wouldn't be afraid of a visit to a hospital when they have knowledge of how their younger sibling was marred during routine medical care. Even if my sibling's problem with the hospital occurred when I was only a year old, part of me still remembered, still knew what happened in a supposed place of healing. The warning that seeped from my very soul was very reminiscent of the slight tinge in my right side that still shows up to remind me: "HEY! You broke your ribs years ago. This intermittent discomfort will stay with you for the rest of your life."

The incident went like this, my mother was sent home with Taylor, happy as can be. When she got home, though, the young infant would not keep any food down. Instead, the child kept throwing it up without fail. Finally, after a few days of not keeping anything down, my family rushed my sibling to the hospital. The treating physicians found that my sibling had a knot in the small intestine. The medical term for the ailment is called *volvulus*. According to what my mother told me, Taylor was suffering from an extremely severe version of the condition. The doctors told my mother that Taylor required immediate surgery, or the knot in the small intestine would lead to any number of potential medical complications down the road, up to and including death.

In a rush to surgically repair the damage, the medical staff at the hospital gave my infant sibling too much oxygen. Evidently, too much oxygen is a *BAD* thing (hyperoxia/oxygen toxicity is the medical term), and Taylor was left with permanent damage to his brain. Not enough to kill him, but enough to cause people to label him as someone in need of special education services later in his life. Regardless, the slight uneasiness in my young mind was hospitals were a place where people could be harmed. So, when my younger self needed blood work, it would take multiple orderlies to hold me down. A child who doesn't want his blood taken, who doesn't trust a doctor, is a patient that can be too strong for one grown man to immobilize.

Not to kid myself into thinking I was stronger than grown adults, but a child who is unwilling to cooperate needs extra care to conform to the requests of the medical staff. The medical staff does not want to hurt a child, but they also need to make sure I was compliant with the doctor's request. But my young mind was in no position to be negotiated with. The orderlies would need to be called on to make sure I was in a calmer state for a nurse or a phlebotomist to collect a blood sample. If I couldn't or wouldn't calm down, something would need to be done to quiet the conflict. Tests would need to be done, regardless of the wishes of a child too young to value their importance.

Eventually, my mom calmed me down, and the medical staff needed to bribe me to take a blood sample. The bribery was so subtle, yet so sweet. I was given a nice cherry-flavored lollipop to satiate my apparent hunger. The extra sweet, chemical-cherry flavor masking a ton of sugar provided a sense of relaxation, a calmness that eased my young, immature mind. Finally, with a sense of peace, a sense of newfound tranquility, I was able to give blood.

Even though that happened in my childhood many years ago, I still believe I have an adverse curiosity whenever my blood is taken. I will begin to hold my breath, clench my fist tightly, and await the potential discomfort. But I do not view needles with the same level of aversion. I now have morbid curiosity about what may happen. I often watch to see if my vein will collapse like Mom's the few times I saw her blood drawn.

I think the real reason, the most logical explanation for my latent aversion towards medical professionals, especially in the realm of mental health, is my secondhand experience with psychiatrists who would rather overprescribe psychiatric medicine in lieu of actually helping the root cause of the issue. For example, my mother had to take one medication and then another medication to help with the reactions from the first medication. The second medication would need an additional set of prescriptions to counteract any problems from all the other drugs. It would continue on ad nauseam until my mom was taking fistful upon fistful of pills. These medications made me feel like the psychiatric healthcare system was overprescribing medication for patients, especially since my Mom was on AHCCCS (Arizona Healthcare Cost Containment System), the state insurance provided to individuals who were extremely poor. The problems were so bad that she would constantly have mental breaks, needing to be committed a few times. My mother even imagined how my father would harm her because of shows she saw on television. Never mind how she was barred from the local hospital because she would strip off her clothes and go running down the hospital corridors.

Imagine if she actually received genuine care intended to alleviate the problem instead of just throwing medications at the problem? Putting people over profits, now wouldn't that be something?

February 22nd, 2019

The week is just a typical week considering what is (NOT) happening during the school day, as I expected with decreased opportunities to practice and experiment with my teaching style to grow as an educator. Ever since I was told about these stupid accommodations because of me surviving a brain injury that occurred over a decade ago, this entire time has been entirely fruitless. I feel more and more unprepared as an educator because Mr. Sona has placed a baby harness on my student teaching. I can only move as far as he will let me, and right now, it feels like he only wants to drag me instead of allowing me to walk on my own.

What is the stigma behind my survival? I am fully aware, and I can do anything I want. I even had to get certification by an outside evaluator for my driver's license to be reinstated due to the apparent medical suspension, a medical suspension denying me the right to drive because I suffered a traumatic brain injury and was placed in a medicated coma. So, I have jumped through all of the hoops: returning to school after a six-year educational gap, further exacerbated by the brain trauma caused by the reckless actions of another; graduating from community college, even doing well in collegiate forensics; graduating from *The University* with academic honors; and finding my dissatisfaction with the employment choices available to me after graduation so I could attend graduate school to get my Masters and teach secondary education.

Mr. Sona even gave me positive feedback for the entire week, stating that I was a good teacher. Overall, I was still receiving glowing recommendations in TK20. So, from just looking at the cold, hard data, everything was above board. I was doing fantastic. I was doing well teaching multiple classes throughout the day, and I would have the ability to just take over my own class.

But even with the positive lies because I am still not teaching or doing anything like that, I am scared about how this is going to affect my career. I can only be student teacher once, and I am not receiving the same quality of teacher training as some of my other peers within the same program. They were gifted the opportunity to take over and teach classes, but I was only getting the same level of training on paper. Suffocation through excessive caution was not the reason why I joined this program. All the hours poring over books and hearing about the experiences of prior teachers was going to waste, dying with a dissipating breath of unmet expectations. Sam, the explorer, who follows the map, follows the routes and journeys of yesteryear finds not the Promised Land but a desolate wasteland, a wasteland where countless educational hours languish with fragments of a dream.

But I was not expecting the deepest cut of all…

After the slew of accommodations they said I needed, limiting my opportunities to gain knowledge and comfort within the profession, my mentor teacher slammed me with the proverbial sledgehammer during the last five minutes before the first bell to start the day.

"I don't see you teaching high school." Mr. Sona said as he stood upright and rigid. He was gazing off into another part of the classroom, avoiding any eye contact with me.

"What?" I said with a perplexed expression upon my face. His statement bore a hole directly through my aspirations of making a difference.

"Someone like you…" Brief pause. "I feel it would be better for someone with your *history* to focus on the younger grades."

"Why? I am doing everything you say and what the program is telling me to do. You guys get paid way more, either way."

"Well, we don't really have a teacher shortage in this distract, especially for teachers in your position. Everyone who works here has almost a decade of experience."

"What? Two of the students who were part of the same Community College program, who received their associate's degree the same time as me, also work here, straight out of college."

"Sadly, you may have more difficulties than other teachers. Therefore, you will likely need extra time and support to be great. You will also need someone to vouch for you."

"What do you mean?"

"I think you should work for a middle school since the information for the students is less. You can spend a few years working in middle school, and if you want to, maybe a high school will take you."

"What? I spent my internship at this school district. Now, I am doing my student teaching here as well. I'm wasting my time."

"No. You're not." He tried to console me after basically telling me I was not good enough. I need to spend extra time working with little kids with little pay to match while other people, people who are not brain injury survivors, could start working for this school district right away.

"Why do I have to work for a middle school," I voiced my inner thoughts, "when all the people that student taught at this school district was able to get teaching jobs at this District when they were done. What is so different about me?"

Mr. Sona did not answer the question, nor did I press him later to provide his response. I just took his first

133

statement to heart, "I don't see you teaching high school." I carried those callous words with me throughout the rest of the day.

When I got home, after I told my partner how I was treated, I decided to email my clinical coordinator Mr. Saille, per *The University's* instructions on what to do when a student teacher is concerned about how everything went down.

The email basically entailed the entire events of what was going on and how I was being treated. As a result, I asked to be removed from the site. Additionally, I had a sneaking suspicion that I was required to remind Mr. Saille how I was a TBI survivor and reminded him of the date when I told all of them during our meeting before school.

I don't know.

Considering the change after I self-disclosed my health history, especially since I wanted to impart why I decided to become a teacher, I feel this entire experience has strayed beyond the original intention. It's leading me to darkness, a void — not towards the light of promise.

Memory before the Arizona Teachers Academy

A lingering damp aroma of struggle permeated my being while I took every step forward into the gym.

The mats were worn.

Every few minutes, the farthest light in the back flickered — in a helter-skelter rhythm that bored into the psyche of every wrestler.

My 9th Grade feet were not allowed to roam free; so, I needed to rely on the school-donated wrestling shoes, originally white and grey but tinged sickly yellow, to make sure I understood how they were not new nor in the best condition. The kind of shoes that would make me believe that a vengeful collection of fungi awaited ne, their next unsuspecting victim. As soon as the shoes were put on, they would descend en masse to conquer my pasty feet. The eventual painful calamity would require ample amounts of ointment that I couldn't afford. With the knowledge of this vengeance resulting from having a mother who collected Social Security Disability and a father who would often spend every dime at the local tavern, a tavern who rewarded its visitors a plastered stumble home, I needed to convince myself that I should join the team in spite of shoes that should not be worn by a person who hates athletes feet.

Part of me felt I did not belong here. This was a club for the strong, testosterone-soaked, alpha males. No matter what I could do or change about myself and my body, I initially felt I would never be considered one of this group.

But as I entered with care, guided by steps that would not ruin the shoes, I saw another 12th Grader. This one was completely different from the rest of the hulking behemoths. First, the wrestler was a she. Second, she was shorter than me by about a foot. If she joined the team, I knew that I shouldn't be scared of not making the team.

The coach looked at me, seeing the nervousness painted across my face.

"Hey, new fish," the coach said with the glowing grin of breaking in students who think they want to wrestle. "We are going to have all of you line up against the padded wall, and I will assign returning members from last year's team to see if you will be on the freshman, junior varsity, or varsity wrestling team."

"Are we going to stretch first?"

"Who said that?!" The coach bellowed.

I raised my hand.

"New fish, I want to see what this wayward school really has." He then smirked. "I want to see if you guys are the real deal."

As the most petite new person on the team, I hoped that I was matched up with the only other person close to my build and stature.

As the coach pointed, jumping around what appeared to be a purposeful random and matched up newbies along the wall with returning wrestlers of the same size, I was beginning to think this wouldn't be so bad.

"You, a match up with *Stretch*." As the order came from the coach, my heart instantly sank. I did not get someone closer to my size and weight. I was matched up with the biggest guy on the team. He was like six foot five. I swear he must have weighed about 260 pounds. He likely outweighed me by over a 140 pounds while also being a good eight inches taller than me.

"He did the same thing to me," the girl said to me, an attempt to make me feel this was a normal rite of passage. She was not, however, matched up with someone who clearly double her body weight.

"Hello," said the mountainous combination of teenage strength, speed, and cunning.

"Hey." I meekly replied.

We walked over to the designated section of the mat and faced off against each other. He stood with both hands hanging down his side, his left foot slightly in front of the right, arching his body forward with a looseness in preparation of competition the second the coach yelled "Go" to start the match.

"Okay, assume the position."

I tried to mimic his stance. I thought the way he conducted himself might give me an edge while also hiding any of my inexperience. My muscles were tense underneath my white t-shirt and gym shorts.

"Get ready…"

I was ready to prove myself. I was prepared to remove any doubt the coach had with me.

"Go."

As soon as the words *go* escaped the coach's mouth, the 12th Grader shot in for a double leg takedown. This maneuver is supposed to quickly down the competition. The result, when hit correctly, is a quick and efficient win, especially against an inexperienced and overmatched wrestler like myself.

Because I didn't know what to do, I kicked back both of my legs in an attempt to avoid his arms as I reached over the top of his back as a way to gain control with my defensive instincts — later, I would learn the move I attempted was called a "sprawl."

As I kicked out in defense, Mr. 6'5" decided to stand straight up. As he stood straight up with full force in an attempt to keep me from gaining control, the top of his head connected directly with the bottom of my chin and jammed my lower row of teeth into the top.

My head snapped back like I had just received an uppercut from a heavyweight boxer, and I stumbled, but I remained on both feet.

The match was instantly brought to an end. Mr. 6'5" apologized and told me that I should sit down for a moment. I felt woozy as I sat down. I didn't cross my legs like I normally would when I sat on a mat. Instead, I just put my left and right hands down by both of my sides. It was an attempt to make sure that I wouldn't tip over.

As I looked forward, my vision blurred. I looked down a dark tunnel whose exit pulled further and further away. I sat utterly transfixed and waited for the sunlight in the gym to vanish.

It did not.

My vision corrected, and I was pulled to the end of the tunnel. I saw everyone else was still trying out for the team. I did not know if I made the team or not. With my short match with Mr. 6'5", I started to comfort myself with the fact that I probably did not make the team.

I rubbed my right cheek. Something was caught between my teeth. I didn't realize that I had something in my mouth from lunch earlier in the day. Maybe the food was knocked loose by Mr. 6'5". As my fingers explored, I did not find food. Instead, it was something hard, and it jabbed my upper, outside gums. I pulled what was like some hard food that sat in my mouth all day, growing stale and disgusting. I prepared myself for the extra sour smell of my unbrushed teeth. The constant decay in my mouth caused my breath to smell like old food and dried blood from bleeding gums.

What I pulled out was thin, off yellow, and very hard. I realized that it was a sliver of one of my bottom teeth. The hard head of Mr. 6'5" almost knocked me out while also causing a sliver of a tooth to separate from my lower molar. I know his head already made my dental condition even more severe. But as I looked at the tooth, I realized that I could have been knocked out in front of all the other wrestlers. I was truly fortunate that I wasn't knocked out.

I took a deep breath, refocused, and the practice continued.

March 1st, 2019

Well, I was not given any feedback this week by Mr. Sona. I guess the information about my request to be moved after the inappropriate comments basically shut down any feedback for this week.

I also had a meeting this week with Mr. Sona and Mr. Saille. It was a bizarre afterschool meeting indeed. Even though I was not given the approval to teach anything due to Sona banishing me to his desk to observe, I was utterly taken aback when Mr. Saille showed up and asked to sit down for a meeting.

As the three desks were taken away from three of the surrounding Kagan pods that made up the teacher's classroom, Sona and Saille exchanged pleasantries about what was happening during the school year, did any student need to be placed on suspension, what kind of bonus they would receive at the end of the year, and other things that had nothing to do with the matter at hand — my request to be placed in another classroom.

"The program decided that we should meet," said Mr. Saille with somewhat exhausted. "We need to discuss how we can work this out."

"Okay," I said, hiding my sense of surprise why all of this was going down.

Mr. Sona sat on the right side of our little triangle. He was reticent. He just looked at me. His face was completely blank, not giving anything away.

Mr. Saille brushed off the desk and sat down. He put his messenger bag on the desk and pulled out his laptop. "We need to talk about the email you sent to me on February 27th."

"What about it?" I asked.

"We don't think it is in your best interest for you to switch placements at this time," said Mr. Saille. "I think you should stay here, finish out your student teaching, and then we will take it from there."

"But what he said…" I trailed off. I needed a moment of composure. "It crossed the line."

"You didn't understand what I was trying to tell you. I was just trying to make you better." Mr. Sona said through a forced smile. The crow's feet at the corners of his eyes gave away the impression he was trying to not yell. If I had not been within his classroom Monday thru Friday for almost two months, I would not have noticed the psychological strain, pressure of not losing his temper (It never really happened with the students, but I did notice when they would not listen and how it took every ounce of his being not to use education as a punitive device).

"We think," Mr. Saille started, "it would really be inappropriate and a little unacceptable for you to switch placements this late in the semester. The student teaching will last only until the end of April. You don't want to burn any bridges this early in your professional career. It could negatively affect you going forward, and we all don't want that."

"Yes." Mr. Sona said in support.

"We know cases of other teachers who didn't quite fit at their placement," Mr. Saille started. "They spoke up, causing a lot of unnecessary attention, and they weren't able to get a teaching job after they were done. We don't want," Mr. Saille reached over and touched near my hand. I recoiled. "We don't want you to be placed into a position where you will have to pay back tens of thousands of dollars in student loans for a degree that you cannot even use."

"I agree with Mr. Saille," Mr. Sona said with a hint of a smile on his face. "Stuff like this would be horrible.

However, you do know that you cannot discharge student loan debt in bankruptcy, right?"

"Uh." I was at a loss for words. Should I drop my complaint and potentially save face and my career in the process? Did it even matter? Did I already harm myself by bringing up my concerns? No matter what I do, they will likely come after me. I really feel like I may be at the point my decision will boil down to being a Sophie's choice, and they may be trying to cover themselves from potential repercussions.

"Uh," I began again. "I think I am going to need a few days to think about it. What you said is a lot to take in."

"Take all the time you need." Mr. Saille had a look of triumph. The kind of look that a person makes when they how they got away with something. It is the look that a person gets when they get A+ on a test they didn't study for and just cheated their way through it.

I got up — my face clearly troubled by all of the news. I started to walk to the door, both educators followed each movement I made to exit the room without giving anything away. They studied how I was reacting. I didn't know what to do, but I didn't want to engage with them any further.

I needed time to think to see if I should say something. If I agree with Mr. Saille and Mr. Sona and just dropped my complaint, would I eventually wind up getting hurt in the long run? Will my decision place me in a position that will hurt my family, my children? Will this hurt our youngest child?

As the door opened, my thoughts kept churning about what I should do and how I should handle the situation. Even when I entered my car and drove home, I was still troubled by the subtext of this meeting.

I was trapped, and I didn't know what to do.

141

Memory before the Arizona Teachers Academy

After receiving the doctor's note for me to return to work, I was in an uncomfortable position of no longer having a car. From the pictures that I received while in the hospital, the right side of the car I was driving was destroyed entirely, caved in by the impact of the red light running vehicle. If someone was in the passenger seat at the time, they would have probably been killed instantly. Thinking about it, we probably both be in an awful way if someone was riding in the car with me. I guess being the only one in the car was the best outcome (even with my injury).

Even though I returned to work full-time, the doctor stated he was unable to medically clear me to drive. Besides, he could potentially be sued for medical malpractice; so, he suggested I attend a driving school where I would need to pay for an evaluation of my abilities. So, until I was able to afford to pay for an outside evaluator to make sure I was able to drive, I was forced back into taking the public transit system (or getting a lot of exercise walking).

The idea of relying on a city bus was a very problematic situation. I felt like I was being punished because of surviving the car accident. My ability to travel from place to place relied solely on the timeliness of the public transit system, a problem exacerbated by the Phoenix's less than ideal transit system. For the size of Phoenix, it really should have a much better system that runs 24-hours a day.

Because of my predicament, because I did not feel like walking almost 10 miles to get home from work, in those opportunities I was allowed to leave work early, I bought myself a 10-speed mountain bike to get home much faster.

Suppose I ever was presented with an opportunity to go home early because the office was overstaffed for the evening or the number of calls from the public amounted to about a call an hour (especially if it was a holiday), I could clock out early and go home because I was no longer handcuffed by the bus schedule. So, in my exuberance from my purchasing decision, I started to take my bike to work every day (just in case).

I took the bike to work every day for about a week.

It was a Saturday night around the holidays. There was a steady downtick of callers from previous nights. So, I knew I would eventually have the opportunity to go home early. Because of the bike, I should be able to get home in about an hour and a half. So, I would be capable of getting home in time to get a little more sleep by hitting the hay earlier instead of taking a cat nap in an office chair at work (pro tip: a traumatic brain injury causes a survivor to become fatigued quicker than the normal population).

"Anyone want to go home?" My supervisor asked.

She worked here for several years. She was lithe due to her diet and constant physical activity at work — pacing constantly — combined with her habit of smoking two packs a day. Yet, even with her smoking habit, she maintained her petite look into her mid-60s, all without an accompanying smoker's cough. I would consider her a marvel to modern science, especially since my Dad has a constant cough.

I raised my hand. I was four hours into my *Friday*, and I would have Sunday and Monday off to relax and watch football if I wanted. Because I would get home so early, I had the option to take a short siesta before an 11 AM kickoff.

"Get out of here."

I was so glad that she picked me because I could not stay here any longer. It was just so dull. I couldn't play video games or surf the web because the business monitored our internet activity. If I was on any website without reason, I would get in trouble for misusing company resources — even receiving a write-up.

Because we were only on the second floor, and I did not want to wait for the elevator, I rushed down the stairs. I went to the patio and the bike area, undid my lock, and I felt the excitement of finally taking my bike home.

The air was crisp, clean, with a slight breeze. There was not a cloud in the sky to obscure the bright crescent moon in the sky. This seemed like the perfect weather to ride home. If it was raining, stormy, or unbearably hot, I would have instantly known that I had made a grave mistake.

As I got on my bike and began to pedal away, I looked back at the office building's dark tinted windows contrasted with the sickly yellow parking lot lights around the building's parameter. I smiled with a deep content that I would not have to stay there another minute.

I rode half a block down 22nd Avenue, taking a left on Dunlap. I began riding towards Metrocenter. The cool air was invigorating, especially since I was riding at a leisurely speed. The streets were mostly abandoned, with only a few sporadic cars traveling either direction through the illuminated tunnel of streetlights.

When I came to I-17, I got off my bike and walked it across all four crosswalks. Because of the incident months prior, I did not want to tempt fate. They might ticket me this time instead of letting me off with a warning.

Instead of riding up and taking a left at 35th Avenue, I rode across the abandoned parking lot of the Toys-R-US and other assorted shops. I rode on the sidewalk next to the northbound lane, crossed the canal bridge by where Monkey Mambo Music once stood, and rode across the empty Metro Parkway. Because the parking lot mainly was vacant besides a few cars, I just cut straight through the parking lot.

The bus station at Metrocenter still had its lights on, and one person was sleeping on one of the seats. It must have been a better place to rest than anywhere else. But even then, I surmised that it would be incredibly uncomfortable.

I crossed the parking lot and went down the S-shaped Cheryl Drive. The multitude of street lights illuminated all the sleeping houses filled with sleeping people. All these people did not have to work the third shift like me, but they likely missed out on the peacefulness of a late night as well. The comfort of solitude enhanced my travels, hand-in-hand, with my thoughts.

When should I switch careers? I should do something that will really help people was my initial collection of thoughts. I really wanted to help make the world a better place. I know I did my little part when I worked for CDC-INFO, but I was really torn by my third shift work.

By working nights, I no longer had time to hang out with friends. By working Tuesday thru Saturday, I missed out on the typical social hours of anyone who would be my peer. I needed something drastically different.

But what could I do? I was in an accident a few months ago, and I couldn't even drive. I did not even have the money to return to go to school. I knew how only having a high school diploma kept many of the doors closed for me, even if the diploma was considered an advanced diploma by my former high school district. So, I was shackled by shiftwork.

I eventually got home a little later than anticipated because I fell down once and walked my bike for about a mile, but I entered my house with a new drive and a new perspective of what I needed to do. I pulled out my cellphone, emailed my supervisor, and put in two weeks' notice. Finally, I would attend college, even if it was almost six years after I graduated from high school.

March 15th, 2019

Well, this week was only different outside of the classroom. I was still not given a chance, the smallest of opportunities, to really instruct the class in any meaningful way. Being relegated to the back of the class, I acted more like a teacher's aide than a teacher in training. So I will chalk this up to another week without a real chance at growth as a future educator. Nothing like being held down, chained down because I was different than the normal candidate in one of the most fundamentally essential professions.

On Wednesday, I was contacted through my school email by the education college to come down for a meeting (primarily uneventful), even though I feel the grains of hope slipping through my fingers. The entire point was to take down what I said, my concerns regarding my treatment by Mr. Sona, and make sure that I wanted to find a new location to finish out my student teaching.

Walking into a personal library masking as an office, Dr. Martins, the Director of Student Placement, sat at his very large, and likely very expensive, oak desk. Besides appearing insanely expensive, the Director's seating arrangement also gave off the air of unquestioned authority. It probably absorbed the tears of many college students. My own constitution was hoping my tears would not join the countless others absorbed into the desk of Dr. Martins.

Next to Dr. Martin sat Prof. Sanchez in an office chair. Because the desk was only designed for one person, and it was likely too heavy or fragile to just push away from the current spot, the back of Prof. Sanchez's chair was firmly against the wall. Clearly, *The University* did not take the time to make the area conducive for a meeting.

As I sat down, I greeted both of them. I did not want to overwhelm by having my lips firmly pressed against their posterior. Instead, I wanted to show that I was a regular, hardworking student teacher who just wanted to move out of a toxic environment.

"Hello," Dr. Martin said with a cheery disposition. I was instantly put at ease. "What troubles you today?"

"Uh, Dr. Martin…" I was unsure of myself. The Director's attitude caught me off guard, considering the gravity of the situation. "Uh, I just think I want to move out of my current placement."

"Why would you want to move?" Dr. Martin asked while Prof. Sanchez just sat there, observing, not saying a word.

"Well, I don't feel comfortable there anymore. Ever since I told them about my health history and about how I felt, things have been different."

"How so?"

"Mr. Sona no longer works with me, no longer gives me pointers, no longer gives me an opportunity or even scaffolds the student teacher program requirements so I get the most out of this experience…"

"Uh-huh."

"…and he doesn't allow me to really lead the class."

"Did Mr. Sona give you a reason why?"

"Well, no. Mr. Saille, my Clinical Supervisor, told me that my responsibilities would be cut back to make sure I get structured practice as a teacher."

"Why did Mr. Saille say that to you?"

"Well, I emailed him a few weeks ago about what my mentor teacher was saying to me and how I was uncomfortable."

"Do you have a copy of those emails?"

"Yeah?"

"Good. You should forward them to Dr. Sanchez and me. We will need to look over them."

"Okay." I said. I wanted to make sure I was being as helpful as possible so this problem gets rectified as quickly as possible.

"Now, about the need to change placements, considering it is so late in the semester, it may be hard for us to find you a new site that will give you plenty of time to the student teacher."

"Okay," I said. "I was wondering what they were trying to tell me."

"So, we are presented with two choices. Option one, you can stay at your current site. If anything happens, you just let us know."

"That makes sense."

"Option two, if we find a new place for you on short notice, we will place you there. Okay?"

"That sounds like a good idea."

"Wait a moment. If you switch to a new site, if anything happens, we will be unable to help you."

"Why is that?"

"Because you made the choice to move, you will be fully responsible for anything that happens to you there. In other words, if this happens again at the new site, you were the one that put yourself in that position by asking to be moved. So, we will be unable to help you any further."

"Okay."

"Keep in mind, if you fail this student teaching, regardless of it being at an old or new site, you will be fully responsible for paying back the entire scholarship. It will be converted to an unsubsidized loan."

"What does that mean?"

"It means," Dr. Sanchez harshly interjected, "you will be charged interest from the very start of the scholarship. Well, it would no longer be a scholarship but a loan. Right now, your scholarship counts for $25,632. If you fail this student teaching, regardless of the reason, the state will sell your loan to a bank, and you will be forced to make payments without a grace period to help you. With one year of interest at 3.5%, backdated to the start of the program, you will likely exit the program, without a degree, and you'll be slapped with a $26,529.12 loan."

"I don't have that kind of money."

"I know," Dr. Martin said. His calming contrasted with his partner. "We want what is best for you. So, before you make a decision, I want to think about it for a moment. Would you rather gut out this current placement, or would you want us to move you? Keep in mind, if you pick the latter option, you run the risk of being financially harmed by the decision. Please think carefully."

I sat there. My mind was racing with all of the potential harm that would befall me if I stayed or left. I did not know how I should approach this choice. Should I stay in a position where I am not allowed to grow as an educator? Even if I remain at MJMHS and pass the internship, would I be really marketable as a teacher? Would I have the countless lesson plans that I could show at a teachers' job fair? I mean, what would I really have to offer for my experience? Nothing and a lot of debt.

My concern of impending financial doom was overshadowed by what would actually happen if I stayed. What could I do if my mentor teacher and *The School District* tried to escalate the matter? It seemed like *The University* was not really on my side, even though I spent $20,000 five semesters to receive my undergraduate degrees in two years after my associate's, even though my degree had guaranteed Arizona taxpayer money attached to it, and the State of Arizona was trusting teacher's preparation program at *The University* to get me into a classroom as a full-time teacher.

But what would it say about me as a person if I just sat there, taking the mistreatment? I couldn't stand idle, ignoring how Mr. Sona and Mr. Saille were treating me.

"I need to be moved."

Memory before the Arizona Teachers Academy

Getting to my job, I would often take the bus. I would take the 35th Avenue Bus all the way to the Mall. I would then take Route 90 down until 23rd Avenue. I would then walk across the parking lot into my old job.

Because I worked the third shift, I needed to take the bus earlier and get to work about 30 minutes early. I was required to take the only bus that would stop at Metrocenter about five minutes before the 90 would arrive and depart. It was even worse on the weekends because the buses would reduce their trips to once every hour.

So, if I was too late for whatever reason; be it the bus was running late, the bus arrived too early, and I missed it, or I was just too late to leave my house, and the 20-minute walk to the bus stop caused me to miss Route 35 bus; I would miss the last Route 90, and I would be forced to walk from Metrocenter to 22nd Avenue and Dunlap.

I would need to walk straight across the Metrocenter parking lot, mostly winding down for the day by the time I would get there, walk through the massive Toys-R-Us parking lot, and I would stop at four crossing signals to get across. Then, if I was in a hurry, I would time my jay walking across each one because it was so much faster than waiting for the walk signal to appear.

Because it would work like a clock and transition from one direction to the next, if I waited on the northeast side of the intersection, I would waste extra time to travel to the other side of Dunlap Ave. So, I would always continue down the road, and I would either jaywalk or wait for the crosswalk at 23rd Ave. Then I would cut across the parking lot to Argosy University, and walk to the front of my office building right off 22nd Avenue, badge in, and work my standard third shift.

One time, because I was in a hurry because I missed my usual Route 35 bus, and I had to wait an extra hour for the next Route 90, I decided to walk the one and a half miles to work from the Metrocenter Transit Center. The air was cool, so I found it very easy to walk briskly to work. However, because I wanted to surf the CDC and university websites for more information about my diffuse axonal injury, there was an extra oomph in my step. Also, it has been said that because the social pragmatics and self-regulation have been washed away by the injury, TBI survivors are a little more impulsive than their non-injured counterparts. So, my need for more knowledge about what happened to me and my potential prognosis would drive me to increase my rate of travel from a fast walk to almost a jog.

I crossed by Toys-R-US, and I was on the straightaway towards I-17. However, the DO NOT WALK sign stopped me in my tracks. Because I just missed the walk sign, I would need to wait for an entire revolution so I could cross the north side of the I-17 southbound lane.

I did a quick mental calculation. I looked down the southbound exit, and I just ran across the crosswalk. When I came to the next section, I jaywalked again because the cars parked in the left turn lane had a red light. I jogged across the entire median, and I came to the left lane to turn on to the northbound lane. Unfortunately, they didn't have the turn signal, and I didn't have the walk sign, so I decided to jaywalk again. Understandably, because I had jaywalked three times already, I was out of sync with the walk signals indicating I could legally cross the crosswalk, meaning I had to jaywalk across the northbound lane and access road to the I-17.

Because I timed everything perfectly, I crossed at my own pace and not times designated by the city. I felt a little rebellious doing this insignificant brush with danger. If I was hit while I was jaywalking, I believed it would be my fault. BUT the most important part was I got away with it.

When I was about half a block away, I looked at my cellphone to see that I would likely get to work about 10 minutes early. That would give me plenty of time to set up, goof around, fill my cup with water, and prepare myself for a slow evening.

Then I heard the police sirens.

I kept walking, looking at my feet as I walked along the sidewalk. I didn't think anything about it.

"HEY!"

A police officer on a motorcycle, riding against traffic, parked off the sidewalk right in front of me. Then two squad cars stopped on both sides of the officer's motorcycle, two police officers came out of each. I stopped in my tracks. I was confused about what was happening.

"We need to talk to you." The police officer said in a commanding voice.

"Uh, what did I do? I'm on my way to work."

One of the officers began to speak, "we received a complaint that someone ran across I-17 about five minutes ago." Someone called the cops because I was jaywalking?

Being shocked and scared, I just spilled the beans: "uh, yeah. I crossed the four crosswalks because I was in a hurry. I didn't want to be late, but I knew when each side would cross because the cycle for the lights to turn and the crosswalks to turn white goes in a counterclockwise fashion."

"No," said one of the officers who came from the squad car that parked on the left side of the cop's motorcycle. "We got a call that someone ran across I-17."

"Well, I crossed the four crosswalks…"

"No, someone from the gas station called and said someone was running across I-17. You know the actual freeway?"

It finally clicked. They were saying that I was crazy enough to go down the embankment, run across the southbound I-17 freeway, jump across the median, run

154

across the northbound I-17 freeway, and then climb up the embankment to get to the other side.

"I wouldn't do something like that," I pleaded. "That's beyond crazy. I was just in a car accident about six months ago. I suffered a traumatic brain injury, a left frontal lobe hemorrhagic contusion, a subarachnoid hemorrhage, both of my lungs collapsed and a lacerated liver because the multiple right rib fractures." I said this as I was pointing to the still pink scar on the left side of my head the ceiling of my car had left me (the scar from the hospital was neater, more careful, and there wasn't a loss of hair in the area) and the still pink mark on my throat from the tracheotomy tube.

I lifted up my t-shirt. "You can see the circular scar from the PEG tube and the other scar when they sliced me open to put in the tube." Funny, at the time, I didn't comprehend how the clearly visible and very prominent scar on my stomach was due to the internal injuries from my broken right ribs.

One of the police officers from the squad car on the left seemed curious about what I was saying. "Yeah," he said, "I suffered a head injury too when I got in a motorcycle crash a few years ago."

"It's crazy," I said, "waking up in a hospital, not knowing where you are and how you got there. Heck, they told my parents how I was going to be in a coma for the rest of my life."

We basically talked for a few more minutes, I promised I would not be that reckless again, and they let me go to work. Fortunately, my supervisor wasn't there when I clocked in because I was thirty minutes late.

March 22nd, 2019

On the Wednesday before my Final Observation at Michael Joseph Mansfield High School, Mr. Sona invited and strongly suggested I attend one of his Teachers' Union events at the main Union building in Central Phoenix. Surprisingly, it appears that the chapter representing their school district also rented out a floor of the Union's office building.

When I arrived there, I parked my car in front. Mr. Sona was already inside, so I just went up by myself to go to my first union meeting ever. The receptionist told me the meeting would be upstairs, I took the elevator up, and I walked into the waiting room.

There was a few petitions to be signed on the table, but no one was there because I was a little late because I didn't realize where members of *The School District's* union would enter the building.

When I finally got into the conference room, everyone was sitting at a collection of long tables that were organized into a giant square that covered the very large meeting room. Everyone was sitting outside the arranged tables, meaning no one was sitting within the hastily arranged enclosure and allowing all eyes to be upfront. Mr. Sona sat on the opposite side of the room from me; so, I was just sitting there the whole time while other fellow school teachers from different parts of the District were chatting with him.

Why didn't he sit next to me? I thought to myself. Mr. Sona was the one who invited me. He could have at least saved me a seat to sit next to them.

The meeting wasn't anything special. It boiled down to nothing more than just a little discussion about how each candidate for union president would best represent the members' needs. It was way above my pay grade. Because this had nothing to do with the class, why did Mr. Sona invite me to this meeting?

On Thursday, I was notified by *The University* about how they could not really find an alternative site for me during student teaching. My only choices were either to go back to Mr. Cichy's class or stay in Mr. Sona's class. If I was not comfortable with the choice, I could just fail the course and graduate without an option for a teaching certification. I would still have my Masters of Education in Secondary Education, but I would be prevented by the Arizona Department of Education from ever becoming a certified teacher.

I was told to notify Mr. Saille of my choice, and I decided to roll the dice and accept the opportunity to go back to Mr. Cichy's class. He appeared to want to do as a little as possible. This meant that I would have more opportunities to work with the class, guide the students through the curriculum, and do all of those little responsibilities given to my other classmates.

Either way, this is my last day in Mr. Sona's class. *The University* finally decided to change my position. Still, I was informed that Mr. Saille would need to do my second observation before transferring to Larry Itliong High School for the rest of my student teacher activity.

So, I stated that we were in the process of reading the 2017 novel by Angela Thomas called *The Hate U Give* this week. I wanted to expand upon the students' understanding of the material since Chapter Two was yesterday's in-class reading assignment. I wanted to expand upon the death of Khalil by opening with three other people who were wrongly killed by police officers: Emantic "EJ" Fitzgerald Bradford, Jr., 21 "Nov. 22, 2018—While trying to save bystanders in a mall shooting, EJ was shot in the back three times by a Hoover Police Offer, who thought he

was the shooter;" Willie McCoy, 20 "Feb. 9, 2019—
McCoy, asleep at a Drive-Thru in Vallejo, CA, was shot 25
times. The officers claimed he had a gun in his lap;" and
Botham Shem Jean, 26 "Sept. 6, 2018—shot in his own
home because a police officer thought he broke into her
apartment."

With that information, I believe the students would
be more than able to understand what was happening in the
world. So, I asked the students to connect what happened to
Khalil to the three gentlemen I listed.

How was it the same?

How was it different?

How would you compare what happened in this
story?

I then connected the opening bell work for the
fallout that would occur in Chapter Three. So, I had the
students read chapter three, stopping at certain portions of
the text to better understand how the Khalil shooting,
inciting event for the main conflict of the story, impacted
the characters during Chapter 3.

For example, I had them read and answer three
sections of Chapter Three: Section 1: "why couldn't Starr
breathe," and "whose death was similar to Khalil's;"
Section 2: "was Starr's response appropriate? Why or why
not," and Section 3: "Describe how Starr's feelings by the
last thing said by Mrs. Rooks," and "How would you feel if
something like this happened to you."

Because the TAP rubric stated one of the items I
needed to accomplish during the evaluation was making
sure the students were on task and working towards
completing the formative assessment, I walked around the
class, making sure the students could maintain stay on tak
and complete the work.

I then concluded the lesson for the day with an exit
ticket asking how they stood on what happened to Khalil,
and what do they predict will happen during the rest of the

book. Logically, I wanted the students to practice imaging what could potentially occur during future events.

The bell rang, and the students started filing out...and something unusual happened. In my previous observation, it was just me and Mr. Saille. But, it was completely different now.As we made our way to the teacher's lounge on Mr. Sona's floor, Mr. Sona decided accompany us and to sit in my post-conference discussion. I know fellow members of my cohort never had something like this happen, or they never talked about it.

Because Mr. Sona invited herself to my final meeting, Mr. Saille and I were led to sleeping pod section of the teachers' lounge. We sat at a circular table closest to a sleep pod near the door (all of them were unoccupied). My mentor teacher stated that he needed to comment right away because his next class was waiting. So, he had the next door teacher, who was on her preparation time, sit in and take attendance while adding his two cents. In a way, I felt this was an opportunity to get his last career-damaging remark about me and my teaching ability. I guess he found the gratification of stabbing the dagger into the chest instead of the back. I think Mr. Sona felt an increased satisfaction of plunging the blade into the still breath chest while the victim can look the aggressor straight in the eyes. He must have felt a sense of excitement from doing this, I know it.

Mr. Sona started, while smiling the biggest shit-eating grin I have ever seen, "I just want to say the student teacher said something incredibly racist during one of my classes a few days ago. I want you to take this into account before you put down the score. It was something along the lines that a student would fail because they were Hispanic."

"No, I did not. You know that I told the student how guilt about performance shouldn't overwhelm any sense of accomplishment. An ACT test is nothing more than a gauge of the socioeconomic status of the parents. It is a predictor of potential academic success. I even told the student about retesting to get a better score in the future."

Mr. Sona, excited by being an apparent whistleblower, "You see? That is confirmation of how the student teacher basically just told how Danny couldn't succeed. So, because you are going to be the clinical supervisor at the next placement, I want you to keep this in mind for all future observations, okay?"

"Okay," said Mr. Saille, trying to hide a hint of a smile on his face. Mr. Sona quickly got up, and he rushed out the door because the third-hour class was waiting...patiently. Mr. Saille turns to me, his face transforming into a mocking look of concern.

"For your lesson plan, I believe it is rated unsatisfactory."

"Why?"

Ignoring my question: "For Standards and Objectives, I am going to give you a three.

"For your presentation, I am giving you a one."

"What? I included visuals, previews, and the information was organized in a logical or—"

Cutting me off, "Classroom activities, I am giving you a three. For Feedback, two."

"But, I answered their questions and helped—"

"Will you let me finish?!"

I just shut down for the rest of the feedback.

"Keeping students on task, three. Teacher knowledge of information, three. Knowledge of students, two. For Teacher professionalism rubric, Part A, professional conduct with others and the school, two. Fulfilling Responsibilities, two. For Part B, content knowledge, three. Seeking feedback, two. Part C, accurate recordkeeping is a two—"

"Why in the world did I receive—"

"Part D, communicating lesson plans to parents, two. Communicate student performance, two. Advocate for students, two. With these scores and the information that Mr. Sona stated, you did not pass this evaluation. Thankfully for you, there will be two other observations for you to earn the threes you need in every area. If you don't, I will be forced to fail you."

"Wait," I finally said, "I only have one more observation. If I pass that one, the last meeting will just be a final check-up to see if my teacher journal is up-to-date. Right? That's what it says on the syllabus from *The University*."

"Well, yeah, but we shouldn't get ahead of ourselves. Mr. Cichy and I go way back; so, I strongly believe it shouldn't be too difficult for someone like you."

I was then told that I was excused for the day, so I went home. On my way home, I got a warning light that my tire was *low air*. Good thing I had tires that would stay inflated longer, but I still had to take it in. I was told that somehow, a nail had gotten lodged into the sidewall, meaning it couldn't be repaired, and I would have to spend about $250 for a new one. I guess another proverbial "fuck you" from MJMHS.

Memory before the Arizona Teachers Academy

I was sitting in the office of my speech-language pathologist at the rehab center. The entire exercise measured if I could hold a conversation with someone while maintaining normal social pragmatics for people without severe head trauma. It was a simple measurement by a friendly discussion.

"How are you doing today?" asked Dr. Williams.

"I am doing alright. The van driver was really funny today. He was really cracking me up."

"Can you describe how you felt being in the backseat of the van?"

"Well, I was just sitting there, and we were kind of talking about movies. I told him I was released from Maricopa Medical Center the day before *300* opened."

"What did you think of that movie?"

"Well, it was like a comic book movie. So, it was okay. But, I was constantly comparing it to Gates of Fire by Pressfield."

"So, you knew a lot about that movie?"

"Not really. It was okay, though."

"Getting back to the main point, what was it like being in the van, talking about a movie, after knowing what happened to you?"

"It was fine. I didn't remember any of it. Dr. Stevens said that because I suffered a brain injury, and the brain was trying to recover from the damage, I was not conscious for the information to transfer from my short-term to long-term memory."

"How does that make you feel?"

"Meh. I don't remember any of it."

"How are your feelings for the other driver?"

"Well, I am here, and I am okay. I don't think it really matters."

"So, no negative emotions?"

162

"No. I am here. I mean, my side hurts where the ribs were broken, but I am still here. I would just like to know why he was in such a hurry."

"That is pretty surprising when you consider what happened to you and how it came about."

"Well, I was talking to a friend last week. They told me, considering my type of injury, how I should have remained in a lower state of consciousness for the rest of my life."

"How did you get such information?"

"Oh, it was the information one of the other providers gave to your company. It was the basic summary that you guys gave to me. The PT guy gave it to me."

"Okay. How did you feel hearing and reading the potential outcomes from your injury?"

"Uhhhh…I feel okay, I guess. I mean, if it was as bad as everyone said, I wouldn't know anything about it, ya know? The one thing that really bothers me is how the lunchroom is very quiet. No one talks to me or anything. It is very boring until I am taken home."

"All the patients we see here are at different levels of cognitive ability than you. So considering some people suffer more extensive damage than you did, or they did not recover in the same way, they may act differently."

"Hmmm…okay. So, a brain injury is like a snow flake. One thing I want to know. I know the witness who saw the accident said how the person ran a red light, but will I ever remember what really happened? I don't even really remember the week before. All the memories I have before waking up in the hospital are all over the place. So, I guess I will never have a clear timeline in my head about what happened right before or even after the car accident, ya know?"

"That is perfectly normal. However, considering the effects of a diffuse axonal injury, you will have holes in your memory," a calm, motherly Dr. Williams said to me.

"Will I ever remember?"

"Do you really want to remember? Looking at the medical notes we received about your condition, I, personally, would not want to remember agonal breathing and what would have caused it. You were severely injured, and the EMTs wrote down you were clearly unconscious."

"I know."

"Imagine, if you will, a two-ton sledgehammer hitting the side of your head at 40 MPH. I want you to think about what kind of damage that would cause. You are very fortunate that you did not have a penetrating head injury. However, your brain suffered extensive injuries. Because of the injury and the loss of consciousness, the memory did not have time to encode into long-term memory, meaning you will never remember what happened."

"So, the only thing I will have is my imagination of what it was like? I will never really know the hurt and all the pain that was caused by the driver?"

"Yes. I think it is best this way."

March 29th, 2019

The air is starting to warm up considerably. The Valley's *winter* is quickly becoming the Valley's **summer**. The upper 80s feels pretty nice, but I am longing for the lows of three months ago. Then, I did not have to worry about having the AC on. I could just enjoy having the windows down and bathing in the nice cool weather. Consequently, it appears those times are soon coming to an end, so I will have to start running my car's inefficient AC, really killing my gas mileage going out to the site of my my student teaching.

It's a good thing this week was Spring Break for both *The University* and *The School District*. I had a week off to really recharge and decompress from every bomb that occurred last week. I know Mr. Saille stated that I would be back in Mr. Cichy's class, but no one from the University has contacted me. If my Clinical Coordinator was correct, why would they place me back into Mr. Cichy's classroom? I hated the drive. No one else in the program needed to drive 20 miles to their school site. I hope I hear something soon about where I am going for the last month of my student teaching. I am really nervous, and I pray I am just stressing myself out just for the sake of feeling stressed. But with the opportunity I have and all the material I am reading and practicing at home, like my days in high school speech and debate or college forensics, I feel I should do well enough where ever I go.

After all, if I am placed into a district that is training a replacement teacher for the next school year, I will definitely be in an excellent position to have a job for the 2019-2020 school year. Then, I can hone my craft in education. I could decide from there if I want to continue being a public school educator, or I could leave and start working in higher academia while earning my doctoral degree. I really want to focus on exploring English or maybe communication, specifically in the field of rhetoric.

I think communication will be a better focus of my future research. I can explore how message construction impacts human development. I guess the area of research I find the most interesting, and I can see myself further investigating, would likely be communication, particularly how complex messages impact brain development. If children are presented with more complex language and more avenues to communicate their wants and desires, their brains will create new pathways to encode and decode information. As a result, their young brains will have improved adaptation skills to succeed in the constantly changing success criteria of our current and future society.

But…if I stay in education, I will likely have a much better impact on society, and I would be rewarded with a much better retirement system after working about twenty-five years or so. I know everyone who works for the State of Arizona has access to the Arizona State Retirement System. I know the overall program is not as good as the teacher pensions in other states, but I guess it is better than just getting a 401K.

I spent plenty of time catching up on the data for my applied project, a project allowing me to earn my master's in education and subsequently receive my teacher certification after I complete the second educator examination (the first educator examination over the subject area was a requirement to enter the program). For my applied project, I am comparing academic performance from one class versus another control group. The research was to see the academic performance increase by starting the class with physical activity, in this case, the physical/vocal warm-ups used by my speech and debate team when I was in high school, versus not utilizing it at all. If it was actual research used for journal publication or discussion at academic conferences, I would need to integrate a sampling method and gather a more significant number of participants than just two classes accounting for around 62 students.

It wasn't a problem because an applied project, as opposed to academically respected research that requires a lot of data to be considered valid, is nothing more than practice for educators to change instruction and accommodate based on how the students respond to the curriculum, I feel this will help set me up for success. But, again, I think it would have been more accurate if Mr. Sona allowed me to monitor how the students performed through my instruction instead of his.

Even though it was not as in-depth as I would like, I still feel that I can write enough, utilizing corresponding research on the effectiveness of organized sports and academic performance, to infer how students would perform if it was part of regular activity. Too bad I was not permitted to write a thesis and work towards a master of arts instead of education, but beggars cannot be choosers. After all, a master of education is a professional degree used by educators and administrators to move up the pay scale, and a master of arts or science is more designed for researchers who want to eventually transfer to a Ph.D. program and use their work to add to the breadth of knowledge. My applied project professor told me that I shouldn't stress about the data as much, considering this is more for my self-reflection. She is just really grading me on whether I complete the assignment on time or not.

Memory before the Arizona Teachers Academy

The uneasiness of reading those words about Mr. Gage lingered with me as I walked in for my next session. The neuropsychologist had the same smile she always does whenever I show up. With the pleasantries out of the way, I sit down.

Her office is friendly, filled with books and other posters about the benefits of therapy after a traumatic brain injury. Heck, the chairs for the patients are extremely comfortable. I could imagine myself falling asleep in one them if I had one at my own house. It was *that* comfortable. Imagine two clouds descending from the heavens, solidifying into solid cushions; those clouds are bound into pleather and affixed to a chair frame.

As I was just imagining the ridiculousness of the image of someone grabbing clouds out of the sky, Dr. Stevens got my attention. I snap back to reality, leaving the small little dream crumbling to dust on the floor of her office.

"Am I going to die in my mid-30s?" I blurted out, remembering what I had read in *Decartes' Error*. This was not a typical way to start a conversation, but my injured brain lacked the patience not to get down to brass tacks.

"What?"

"The book you suggested I read said Phineas Gage died quickly in his mid-30s. Then, like he was minding his own business and popped like a soap bubble just floating along with the summer breeze, he suffered a seizure and died. Is that going to happen to me?"

"Have you had any seizures yet?"

"No."

"Well, if you don't have any seizures within the first year, your risk from dying from status epilepticus falls to the same rate as the general population without brain injuries."

"So, I don't have anything to worry about?"

"Well," Dr. Stevens started to tell me, "the longer you go without a seizure, the lower the probability is of you suffering from one. I understand your concern about how Phineas Gage suffered from that condition, but if you look at the book, it mentions that not much is known about Mr. Gage. Since it was the 19th Century, I can assure you their recordkeeping was not as thorough as we have it today. If Mr. Gage suffered from seizures all the time, how often was he rushed to the hospital? Did they even have hospitals comparable to our own back in the 1800s? So, the longer you go without suffering from a seizure, the less you have to worry about one happening to you. Point of fact, if you do not suffer from a seizure within the first year post-injury, the likelihood of you suffering one reduces to the same probability as the general population."

With the answer to the question putting me at ease, washing away my ultimate concern for a quick and untimely curtain call, I returned to working my hardest to get back into a mentally passible shape. My drive through my existence was no longer a confinement nor imprisonment in a home for the disabled. I would no longer just play video games to wallow in imaginary places. A new will bent me towards an alternative future, one that the medical professionals never thought I could ever achieve. I decided my focus needed to be on truly recovering instead of slowly marching on the drumbeat into nothingness.

April 5th, 2019

On Sunday, March 31st at 5PM, the Teachers College sent me an email regarding where I would be student teaching on Monday. They basically confirmed Mr. Saille's statement that I would need to travel all the way down to Larry Itliong High School to finish out my student teaching assignment. That means that I will have to spend almost two hours a day, 10 hours a week, driving round trips to the LIHS and home. On the days I have to go down to the University, that is even more time and gas mileage I cannot really afford.

Since student teaching is regarded as a full-time job, meaning I don't have the time to plan for class, drive to and from the student teaching site, have time to seek additional employment, work a job outside of my student teaching time to just compensate for the extra money I will need to spend on gas because of the increased mileage going back to and from LIHS, I am fucking screwed. I really hope my family can afford the extra money because my gas take is going to need larger meals every week. I don't know how to manage any of this, considering I am not working because this class is required to get my teaching license. I don't know what I am going to do for gas. Selling blood seems like the only way we can earn extra money. My spouse's job pays just enough to cover all our bills, but I don't want late payments to screw up our credit score...

Hmmm...I can also ask work weekends doing landscaping stuff with my Dad to tide me over until I start my teaching job in July (isn't that when teachers usually start?). I know it will be a tough couple of months until I get the relief of being under contract. I know I will not want to skip too many meals, especially if I am selling blood.

About the classroom, instead of being placed in the equivalent grade level of Mr. Sona's class, the University also confirmed how I was put back into Mr. Cichy's. Additionally, instead of taking over his entire class schedule to get the feeling of a full schedule, I was forced to only teach only the 11th Grade class during the third period. The class no one wanted when the other teacher quit and Mr. Cichy took over for extra pay. In other words, I am only given one class period of instruction.

During the rest of the time, I am supposed to sit in the back during the other five classes because he is preparing them for some massive assignment. I cannot even leave to work at a paying job or anything because he *may* need me to help out. This is complete and utter bullshit.

Because I have nothing to do during the other class periods — besides being bored out of my mind, I would try and just sit down and wait until I am needed, but he just yells at me to get up and stand like I'm in boot camp or something. So, per usual, when I start moving instead of staying in the back because I am antsy (and this isn't the military where I am required to stand at attention for a commanding officer), I get yelled at for making the students uncomfortable because they come from a "troubled homes."

Even when it is the start of the class, and I am supposed to take attendance, Mr. Cichy will just take the attendance himself because he doesn't want "someone like me" to mess everything up. So, no matter what is on the agenda for the day, my day is basically me sitting there for about five hours, bored out of my mind. Then, when I get a chance to teach, the students are entirely uninterested in listening. I even asked for the syllabus for the class, he told me he couldn't provide it for me. When I looked to see if anything was published on the District's website, I came up empty. This is to keep the parents from having an opportunity to berate the teacher for whatever is potentially on the curriculum during the semester.

My God. The amount of suck this student teaching has turn into would require an entire planet. No, an entire galaxy to house the amount of suck. It would have its own fucking gravitational pull, compressing everything down into a singularity of ass. They are really fucking me over. I really feel like I'm being fucked over because I spoke up and spoke out against someone buddy-buddy with some fucker of darkness ruling from on high.

I need to keep telling myself that we have a teacher shortage, and they are probably just putting me through the wringer so I will get used to the potential conflicts of working with other teachers. That is the most likely scenario.

Oh, I forgot the icing on the cake! Mr. Cichy entered his score at 10:15 AM on Thursday, April 4th, meaning I had not even completed the entire week before he made up his mind on my weekly score. Fuckface said I did not act professionally, even claiming that I slept during student teaching, and he let me sleep for hours, telling the students not to interrupt me. Not only is that completely illogical (a class full of teenagers wouldn't let anyone sleep), but I don't know what his game is. He even said that I threw paper at a student instead of giving it to them — because obviously, I am too lazy to just walk in a classroom to pass back a piece of paper.

What Mr. Fuckface was really trying to say from out of the chasm of his own ass: At the end of the second period, as the students were leaving, Mr. Cichy finally told me the students were reading F. Scott Fitzgerald's *The Great Gatsby*. Since I was notified on Monday only right before the class, and I responded that I had nothing prepared for the book (and I didn't know the chapter they were reading), Mr. Fuckface taught the lesson himself. Evidently, he uses the impossibility of being prepared on

172

Monday without even knowing what the students should be reading until minutes before they entered the class as a statement of my professional ability or even using it as an example of performance.

He says that he let me fail so I could understand what it was like coming to school unprepared. But, instead of helping me, especially when I asked him for the class syllabus and sent him emails asking what he was teaching since Sunday night when I found out I was back in his class, he ignored the emails.

Additionally, the statement about where I am acting inappropriately towards students in any way is complete major league bullshit. If I had done anything like he claimed, I would have been run out of the school and the program entirely. I don't know what is going on. Why are they doing this to me? I thought student teaching was supposed to get more support than I am receiving. I know I can do the job, and I am more than willing to teach, but my mentor teacher is really trying to kill my love of the profession.

I complained to Mr. Saille, but he said there was nothing to worry about, and he said it was part of the process. I am really starting to lose confidence in the entire program because they ignore my request to investigate my concerns about teacher misconduct, particularly against me. Maybe I should just stay there and take it, even though working with Captain Fuckaroo is working my last nerve. I really want to teach and make money, but they are making it so difficult for me.

As a small olive branch, Mr. Saille told me he wanted to schedule a time next week to go to Jamison Mills High, the school he teaches at, and I would get some information for my observation in two weeks. I guess he is going to tell me what to do so I can potentially do better in the long run. If he is going to assist me in providing the resources promised so I can pass this class, I see no problem. I guess this will get things rolling, allowing me to stumble across the finish line.

Memory before the Arizona Teachers Academy

It was about a week before I was discharged from the Maricopa Medical Center. I still had the percutaneous endoscopic gastrostomy (PEG) tube in my belly. Apparently, I was told they needed to wait a few weeks before they could safely remove it. So, I was forced to go to the County Hospital with an unused PEG tube still running from my stomach for a few more weeks to make sure the area healed completely. The doctors had to make sure I was completely comfortable having the tube in place for a few more weeks. A premature removal could potentially cause me an even worse medical mishap.

During all the physical activities or anything medically necessary during rehabilitation at the hospital, the tube coming out of my stomach constantly reminded me of what happened to me. My fingers would feel the plastic holder for the tube stitched into my body, the tape holding down the feeding tube so it wouldn't get caught on anything, and the bandages and tape covering the still-healing wound. I would get sick to my stomach, visualizing what would happen to me if the tube got caught on something and disemboweled in the process.

When it was finally time for to remove the feeding tube, two doctors came to my room, an attending physician and what I thought to be an intern. One doctor appeared to be in his late-40s, early 50s with dark eyes and brown hair with streaks of grey. He was wearing a white doctor's overcoat, a white button-down shirt, and black pants. I couldn't see his shoes.

The younger intern, who was wearing a similar outfit, but his pants were tan instead of black, appeared to follow the directions of the older doctor. The older doctor handed him a pair of scissors and began to instruct him to start the procedure. It was dark out, and I was not taken to an operating room or anything, probably because PEG tube removal is must be simple. So, I just had to lay down and look at them as they began their work. All they had to do was clip the stitches that held the external bumper in place and pull out the tube. The intern reached down and pulled the tubing out of my stomach.

The sensation was utterly foreign to me. I have never experienced feeling a tube slide from my inside. It wasn't painful or anything, just bizarre and a completely different sensation than I could have ever imagined. Internal nerves firing off while the tube slowly slide out of a hole in my stomach, I never knew what it would feel like slowly being disemboweled, but I guess it would be kind of like this — just with a lot more pain. After they left, I knew this was something I would never want to experience again in my lifetime.

"You will be going home soon," said the older doctor.

His intern didn't say a word, just smiled.

Once they were done pulling out the tube, they covered the area with a bandage and promptly walked out, wishing me a good night. I watched them walk out of my room, and I laid back in my bed. I reflected on how this was a completely new experience, and I would be going home to put back together what was once torn asunder by a red light runner.

April 12th, 2019

This is beyond horrible. Mr. Cichy is not doing anything to help me grow as a teacher. It was still the same uninteresting tedium of being denied a chance to fly, to soar. I, too, am singing for freedom, pleading for release from this childlike servitude that others place on me, fellow educators place on me. A cycle of repeated, repetitive denials as my hope only circles around the drain of time.

You can't do it.

You need more time.

You may find it too difficult.

You.

You.

You.

Well, **I CAN**, but I am being prevented, denied from fulfilling all of the requirements of my student teaching, and I was treated basically like an over-educated teacher's aide. The fear, the anxiety, and all of the concern about my success during this entire time were for naught, was wasted because people like Mr. Sona, Mr. Cichy, and Mr. Saille did not want me to become a teacher. If I had never received permission to grow, to blossom, how was any one of them so sure that I could not succeed in this profession? What prejudicial thoughts permeated the pair's idea of what made a proper teacher? Does a person like me bring down the public's perception of what is required of an educator? Did I not fulfill some hidden checklist of what makes a paragon of education? If they acted this way with me, what does that mean for students they don't like? Is that why *The School District* is not the best performing one in the entire state?

Either way, I was notified by the University about how they could not really find an alternative site for me during student teaching. My only choices were either to go back to Mr. Cichy's class or stay in Mr. Sona's class. This false dichotomy was the only option provided to me, locking me within only two chambers where I would not *truly* escape. At the same time, *The University* and *The School District* are absolved of any discrimination claims or mistreating a person who may be perceived as someone with a disability. If I was not comfortable with either choice, I could just fail the course and graduate without an option for a teaching certification. I would still have my Masters of Education in Secondary Education, but I would be prevented by the Arizona Department of Education from ever becoming a certified teacher.

I was told to notify Mr. Saille of my choice, and I decided to roll the dice and accept the opportunity to go back to Mr. Cichy's class. He appeared to want to do as a little as possible. This meant that I would have more opportunities to work with the class, guide the students through the curriculum, and do all of those little responsibilities given to my other classmates.

After I made the decision, Mr. Saille informed me of the repercussions of my choice:

"Because you have two more observations…"

"One. The fourth meeting at school does not count since I should have 3s in all the categories by then."

"Okay, but we need to get you to all threes before you can worry about ending at only three. You will not have enough time to get comfortable before we need to get all the observations finished."

My clinical coordinator gave me an assignment he called "Dissecting Gatsby." This assignment, per Mr. Saille, covers all the bases. If I want to pass the course without question, this is the assignment I will teach this or else. However, as I looked over the one-day project for my observation, I felt it was not challenging enough. Me, being me, and understanding how such a choice was shortchanging the students, I wanted to do something a bit more involved. I wanted to have them actually connect the actions of Jay Gatsby, Nick Carraway, Daisy Buchannan, and others.

Because an English class is supposed to give the students the skills to derive meaning from the text; because this is precisely one of the Arizona State Standards, "11-12.RL.1. Cite strong and thorough textual evidence to support analysis of what the text says explicitly as well as inferences drawn from the text, including determining where the text leaves matters uncertain;" I believe the assignment will help me pass the course, make it easier, but it will not really benefit the children as much. Being a teacher is not about what is easy for me, and everything about what will do the best for the students. Education is a selfless profession. I would be shortchanging the students and myself if I become egocentric and only how I did with my third observation.

So, instead of the students just doing what I believe to be a low-level Dissecting Gatsby assignment — a prime example of what I always called "busy work," I will have the students break down each character's motivations. Then, while they are working on that section, I will ask them to connect any people the students know, celebrities they know, or anyone else they believe relates to those specific characters. If I coach them to complete the work correctly, I anticipate the students will find a deeper understanding of what was written by F. Scott Fitzgerald and how it connects specifically to their own lives.

The experiences of fictional characters like Carraway and Gatsby should surely relate to the students' own experiences. Carraway, the man with nothing and trying to make a fortune, befriends Gatsby, who appears to have everything. Through the story, I will help the class uncover the more profound hidden morality within the pages by guiding their thinking through my strategic

179

questioning, allowing them to discover their own understanding of the truth within the human condition.

Once uncovered, the message is not easily cast aside. It is not ignored. It cannot be thrown out with yesterday's garbage or shoved down the garbage disposal. Ideally, it is reckoned for what it really is, a fundamental truth of what it means to be a good person. Because the students are at such a young and formative age, even if they are only 11th Graders in High School, they will come to appreciate, accept, and value what is truly good. My students will know how the materialistic, just like Gatsby, will be left dead, floating in the pool of time. The student, being young, believe wealth and materialism is more important, more lasting. The book will tell the students the fragility of what they value. Such things are discarded, not because they are valuable but because of the ease of replacement.

If a teacher can connect the material, showing how the message and themes transcend the time the work was written, the students will gain something more profound flowing deeper, farther into their very spirit. The message will coalesce with their own psyche, molding them into people who can better understand and appreciate who they are and where they will travel on this beautiful, blue-green world zipping around the Sun. If a teacher like myself cannot give them those gifts, who will?

One negative from this week, though. I couldn't go to school on Friday because I was sick with a splitting migraine. So, I emailed Mr. Cichy early in the morning, and he responded that he would take care of it and take care of myself.

Memory before the Arizona Teachers Academy

The moments would come, not too often but often enough, where we ran out of food. It was usually after the first of the month, meaning our family could be waiting weeks for food. The option of a food box represented one of those unexpected treats that occurred to us when we were in kindergarten through fourth grade. The same option was not available to us now because Taylor and I were in middle school. Teenagers do not carry the same weight as younger children, especially if they are in need. Even if we are too young to work, the food banks will not give us the view us as being that needy. There would be families who were in far worse straights than us, and they would need help just as much. Also, they couldn't afford to provide my family with a weekly supply of food, all of the State and Federal aid my family received should have offset our need for supplemental food.

The pang in our bellies reminded Taylor and me of our lot in life. We were the children who would do without. Hunger was our friend and enemy, gently holding our hand or dragging us along. Whenever it showed up, we would try to do whatever we could to forget it, but such activities were often for naught. The pain would be there all the same.

Sometimes, to get a few dollars to get a loaf of bread and some bologna or those little packages of cheap deli meat labeled as "ham" or "chicken," my sibling and I would have the option to panhandle for a few extra dollars, or we could go around the neighborhood, carrying a trash bag, and pick up aluminum cans to recycle them at a recycling center along Cave Creek Rd, between Mountain View Road and East Vogel Avenue.

Because we could not stand panhandling, making ourselves prostate to gain a few extra dollars, we always picked the option of going around the neighborhood to find cans. We would always do it around 6 or 7 AM because our classmates would not see us, and we would be early enough to beat the other people who wanted those cans for whatever they want, not food in our bellies.

Because my Dad worked Monday thru Friday as a day laborer working in the far North or East Valley, he was often way too tired to do anything when he got home besides grab a beer and watch television. Our Dad gave us clear instructions of where to walk and where to go. We weren't allowed to return until we made enough money so we could have sandwiches at night. This would involve walking up an area that covered from as far west as Cave Creek to as east as 19th Street. The northernmost point was around East Cortez Street, while the southern edge was around East Hatcher Road. That was where we operated.

The early morning air was thankfully crisp and clean with morning dew in the late fall and winter, while spring and summer brought an increased level of heat throughout the day. Regardless of the season, the rule was to start around 6 AM on Saturdays and usually finish around 10 AM. This served two purposes: our friends would almost always be asleep when we started, and Friday night parties usually resulted in a bounty of empty beer cans ripe for recycling.

Houses of different styles and architecture lined all of the streets we traveled. Most of them were white. But, there were tan and brown houses to break up the mix. They were the pox marks of a melting pot of different levels of the poor and middle class. More "luxurious," brown or tan houses were occupied with people who had more money, or they wanted to look like they had a bounty. With peeling paint and grey brick underneath, the homes with flaking off-white paint due to dirt and other eyesores were almost always decades older and in disrepair. But, the families were comfortable where they lived, knowing their place was their own, and they didn't have a landlord telling them what to do.

For us, as we walked the deserted, early morning streets from our apartment at 1301 E. Mountain View Rd, we looked around and realized we had no reason to judge anyone. My family was objectively worse than them, no matter how I thought they were poor. They could afford to live in a house. We were stuck in apartments, looking out to a world where there was a clear divide between my family and our classmates.

We would always pass by this apartment complex and trailer park on the northeast corner of East Cinnabar Ave. and 13th Street during our little treasure hunting trip through the neighborhood. There stood a phone booth at the corner. No one used it. It just kind of stood there, unwanted and unloved.

Years later, I would spend hours talking to whomever I was dating or trying to date at the time. My family obviously couldn't afford a house phone or a cellphone, so this was the best approximation available to me. I would always find a quarter or a few coins, and I would just sit there for hours talking and talking. But during that time, we did not think about ever using that phone during this point in our lives. We were hunting for whatever would allow us to gain money to eat that night.

It was a long and tiresome journey, and if we walked at a good enough clip; both of us would be done before 10 AM, regardless of the outcome. On the good days, we would have more than enough to get some candy as extra. A just reward for our working so hard. On the bad days, we would usually come home empty-handed, with empty bellies the prize for the night. Sometimes, we could only scourge up enough money to get one of the items, likely some cheap lunchmeat to make the old-fashioned *hand sandwich*, or just have barely enough to get by being either a penny or two over or short. The cashier would feel sorry for us, and we would have our little pitiful bounty to feed us for a night. But regardless of the outcome, regardless of how much a bounty we could bring home, we always would have just enough to put the pains of hunger at bay…at least for a little while.

April 19th, 2019

    Well, today was my third observation. I was waiting for both my clinical coordinator and the outside observer to enter the room. Typically, they delay entering the room for a few minutes into the lesson. Once they enter the room, everything that occurs within the class is fair game to be scored: how I communicate with the students who are attending; how I guide the lesson; how the students respond to everything I say and do; the ways I maintain class composure throughout the instruction, guided practice, and independent practice; how I discipline off-task students; etc.

    I guess the evaluators delay in entering the classroom gives the teacher enough time to calm down the students, who typically take a moment to let out their excitement and chattering back and forth from the talking during the passing period. This is why bellwork is effective because I find it easier to tell the students to focus on the assignment on the board.

    As the 11th Graders started entering the class, I greeted them as they walked in while Mr. Cichy moved to the back of the class. I also had the presentation up with the topic of the class period (an analysis of Chapter Seven of *The Great Gatsby*). So, first, I go through the standard bellwork procedure, and then I transition into the lesson with prompts on the presentation: the objective, the state standard, all of it.

    Then the pair of evaluators Mr. Saille and a women I have never seen before walk into the classroom. The University sent down an older lady to be the second observer for my observation. She wore a light-blue blouse, bright rainbow pants, and white tennis shoes. I didn't say

185

anything because that would throw me off and disrupt my delivery. I just smiled as they came in.

Now, instead of doing the work Mr. Saille said would be a way for me to pass the required student teaching course, the Dissecting Gatsby activity, I had them work on answering and explaining the meaning of specific sections of Chapter Seven with their shoulder partner. Since they were supposed to complete the assigned reading over the weekend, since I told Mr. Cichy that the students should read the assignment while I was gone, I felt pretty confident this would go over easy. But, unfortunately, as I was talking about the work and asking questions to see if their thinking aligned with my expectations for this particular lesson, I saw the students had a puzzled look on their faces. It was like I was speaking German or something. So, I stopped, and I asked one of the students near the front if they covered the reading assignment over the weekend.

"No," said a male student in the back. "Mr. Cichy had us silently read any book we wanted all class period on Friday."

"Okay," I said, thinking of a way to pivot into getting the class back on track. "We are going to read Chapter Seven to ourselves. This worksheet analyzes the chapter; so, I would like you to work on it with your shoulder partner while reading. All of ya' got it?"

Silence.

"Any questions?"

Silence.

"Since you guys don't have any question, begin."

As the students were reading, I moved through the classroom, making sure the students were doing everything they could. Every few minutes, I would look over to see if the observers and Mr. Cichy gave away how I was doing.

Nothing.

186

So, I continued to walk around, helping the students who needed it, coaching the students who were having problems understanding the questions and basically doing everything I could to make sure the students were staying on task. Of course, it could have been a better day of instruction, especially if the students were prepared when I was gone on Friday, but I believe I salvaged the lesson even though it was not an optimum performance.

I transitioned the students to their exit ticket, and the ending of my third observation was within my sight. I firmly believed I earned at least a three in each area, but no one in the back was giving anything away. It could go either way.

When the bell rang, the students cycled out of the classroom. When the last student was gone, and it was just the four of us, Mr. Saille asked, "Is there a teachers' lounge or an office where we discuss the evaluation?"

"I can show you," I said. I had been here for a while now, counting last semester and the last few weeks since I was forced back by the University.

"No, you stay here," said Mr. Cichy. "I'll show them where to go, and we will have a little conversation. Then, I'll come and get you in about 20 minutes."

So, I waited, running back everything that was going through my head. Did I do well enough to earn at least a three in every category so I can remove the stress of student teaching out of my life? I hope so. I wouldn't want to do this anymore.

After a little under 15 minutes, Mr. Cichy returned and sent me to meet with the observer and Mr. Saille. So, I hope I hear good news when I come in.

But when I got there, only Mr. Saille was there. I never got the name of the second observer, regretfully.

"Hey."

"Hello," the clinical coordinator said with a smile.

"How did I do?"

187

"We need to go over your scores. Can you have a seat?"

"Anything wrong?" I asked while I sat down in an office chair where the left-back leg felt shorter than the right. Then, as the rocking motion distracted me as I was sitting down, I told Mr. Saille to excuse me for a moment. Subsequently, I walked to the other side of the break room, sat on the nearest chair, saw that it didn't rock, and I brought it back and sat in front of Mr. Saille.

"Sorry about that. So, how did I do?"

"We have to decide what to gonna do from here. You didn't pass the observation.—"

"How?"

"We will get to that. However, because you didn't have the state standard written on the board and the lesson plan did not match up with what you gave during the observation, I am going to say you failed this observation."

"What? The state standard was on the presentation, and Mr. Cichy didn't do anything I told him to do. When I sent the email on Thursday, he never responded."

"So, you should have been here."

"I was sick."

"People come in sick all the time. You're a teacher."

I went on how I sent over all the information to Mr. Cichy the Thursday before, but Mr. Saille continued that it was my fault the students weren't prepared for the lesson. So, with this failure for my third observation, I was forced to complete a, now required, fourth observation on Monday. I asked if there was anything that I could do to pass this final observation, so I don't fail the class, so I don't fail the student teaching assignment, and I don't have to pay back the entire Arizona Teachers Academy grant.

His response was one clear command: "you'll figure it out."

Memory before the Arizona Teachers Academy

After ignoring my friend through 9th and 10th Grade about joining our high school speech and debate team, I finally decided to do it beginning of 11th Grade. I didn't need to buy a suit since it was only a high school team like I would eventually be required to do in community college for forensic competitions. Therefore, I just settled and went to the thrift store and bought a formerly-used button-down collar dress shirt, a belt, and some slacks.

Once a month, we would go down and compete at a high school tournament. The best part about being on our team was the parental involvement. Compared to other schools, whose parents did not really participate, our team would take over a lunch table or two filled with all kinds of snacks brought in by the parents to keep the entire team fed. I learned a few of the competing squads would look upon our tables with envy. So, I guess it was a point of pride that I happened to go to a high school where speech and debate was serious business for some families, families with money no less.

For someone living out of a duplex with no hot water, every monthly competition was a godsend. Also, since we didn't really have to worry about who could join the team (basically anyone could if they wanted to), it was nice that I didn't really have to worry about not making the cut. So, I would try my best to get involved, practice when I remembered to, and make a mental note of when I would get some excellent food while at the tournament.

During my 12th Grade year of high school at the 4A State Speech and Debate Tournament — the final one of my high school career, I pulled out a new piece to perform in the drama category, Robert Bloch's "Enoch." Robert Bloch, the famous writer who penned the 1959 novel *Psycho*, had a nice little short story in his *Pleasant Dreams:*

Nightmares collection. I found the piece incredibly fun to perform during my last hurrah in high school speech and debate.

The heavily-edited version, because all performances had a 10-minute time limit and had to be school-appropriate to an extent, was about a crazy loner in a swamp named Seth. For my performance, I edited out his name because there is a power to a name. The lack of a name adds an air of mystery because it could be anyone, anywhere.

Seth is accompanied by this tiny, invisible creature who sat on his head or shoulder and apparently left scratch marks from his claws. The little fiend was called Enoch. Like any living creature, Enoch would get hungry, but his appetite was for something a little more offensive to a civilized society, human brains. To satiate his little friend, Seth kills any unsuspecting motorists who happen to get lost near his house, beheads them, and dumps all the evidence into the swamp. After the dirty deed is done, Enoch leaves Seth to enjoy the contents of the victim's severed head. While Enoch was feasting on the victim's brains, the creature would leave Seth in a euphoric state.

Everything is going well for Seth until his victim is a female motorist. He kills her, just like all the other victims, but she is different. People start really looking for her, really trying to find her killer. Well, they uncover her car because he didn't hide her well enough, and he is brought in for questioning. During the interrogation, Seth explains everything to the police officer about how Enoch ordered him to kill. Seth was clearly a simple man who lived in the woods. He thought the whole practice was just part of his typical routine, his sole purpose for existing. Thinking Seth is obviously crazy, the police interrogator asks Seth to give him Enoch, so the defense or the jury doesn't see that the murderer is clearly insane.

Later that night, the officer returns, screaming and pleading for Seth to take back Enoch. He talks about how the little creature tells him to do horrible things and what will happen if he doesn't do them. The officer finally convulses and collapses because Enoch kills him, likely separating his brain from his person. Seth comments that he hears Enoch making all the happy sounds when meaty brain morsels fill its little belly. With the officer dead, Enoch's hunger temporarily satiated; Seth welcomes Enoch back, grabs the keys from the officer's pocket, lets himself out, and escapes to an unsuspecting world.

I would really play up the part on how he was really crazy. During most of the performance, I would be uneasy, nervous, quiet, acting like I was unhinged. When it came to the scene where he murders the woman motorist, I pantomimed chopping off the lady's head while yelling out at the top of my lungs in the process. I used it as an attention-getter and a contrast to the low volume insanity of Seth, and I believe it was pretty effective.

As I said, the first and only time I performed the piece was at the 4A Speech & Debate State Tournament my 12th Grade year in high school. I was so nervous about how people would buy into it. Would they hate it? Would they love it? I didn't know. There is a certain grandeur with playing the bad guy, though, especially if the performance unnerves the audience. That was what I was trying to do with my "Enoch" performance.

When I got into the classroom, a male judge was sitting in the back, three other male competitors sitting scattered around the room, and a girl with black hair, brown eyes, and glasses sitting in the center. She was smiling, appearing very friendly as I was called up to perform. She became my point of focus for the piece. At the end of my "Enoch" performance, as I talked about reaching down, pulling the keys from the dead police guard, I looked straight at her. The shutter of Enoch's return caused a fake look of ecstasy to wash over my face. I opened the door, and I was free. With the piece completed, I looked straight ahead: the girl was no longer smiling. Instead, what once was a friendly smile was replaced with a look of disgust that had slowly crept over her face.

Unfortunately, because my pride blinded me to the finer details of what it takes to win in speech and debate, because I did not ask the judge for time signals to know when I had two minutes, one minute, 30 seconds, and then 10 seconds in remaining on the timer, my self-assuredness caused me to lose track of time. My first round went a full 11:00 minutes, a full minute over. I automatically ended with fifth place in that round. I slimmed down the piece even more between the first and second rounds, but the damage to my overall score and my possibility of placing in the tournament was already done. I never broke to the semi-finals with the piece, and I never performed it again, even in college. Apparently, the supernatural doesn't work well at the higher, collegiate levels, at least according to my forensic coaches.

Looking back on that tournament, running over the allotted time, not practicing as much as I could have, I am really bothered by spoiling my one opportunity to do the absolute best in a high school speech and debate tournament. It still bothers me to this day. I think I would have maybe broken through to at least the semi-finals if I actually took more time practicing, took more time preparing for the State.

Out of the two years of competition, I only wound up earning a 6th Place Duo-Interpretation award at my first tournament by doing the piece "Who's on First?" by Abbott & Costello. So, I came so close to winning in an individual event, but it never came to pass because I failed to spend extra time working on the timing of my piece.

C'est la vie.

April 22, 2019

So, today was I had my observation during the third period. I had plenty of time to prepare myself because Mr. Cichy had all the other classes silently reading to themselves, meaning I did not have an opportunity to really practice my lesson with the previous classes. Even if they were a higher grade level, I could still practice an assignment aligned with the state standard I was teaching. I was robbed of taking notes on what I may do differently when Mr. Saille and the outsider observer showed up. I only had one opportunity to pass or fail.

I went down to the copy room before school started to print out all the required material for the lesson. The students only needed the Dissecting Gatsby assignment. I also printed out a few sheets of paper that had a feedback form. Since all of my college courses had professor feedback at the end of the semester, and this would be my last observation for my student teaching, I wanted to get feedback from the students about what I did right and wrong. It was also a chance for the students to feel like they were invested in their own education. I would hand out a simple, short survey in the last two minutes of class (after the students answered their exit ticket). I asked three questions: what was your favorite part about the assignment today, what was your least favorite part, and how would you rate me on my instruction today.

Typically, it is better to try out the lesson plan in the other classes before the planned observation. Then, if changes needed to be made on the amount of content or the overall delivery required a minor adjustment, I would have more than enough time to internalize and formulate appropriate changes to avoid a low score on the TAP rubric. Still, I was not given such an option since Mr. Saille only had the one class of 11th Graders he took on because he wanted more money. So, I would only have one shot to get this right.

When it was judgment time, I was ready.

As the students entered the class, I greeted them as I typically would. The state standard was on the board, "*11-12.RL.1. Cite strong and thorough textual evidence to support analysis of what the text says explicitly as well as inferences drawn from the text, including determining where the text leaves matters uncertain,*" providing the students a preview of what we would be doing (and also allowing me to earn easy points).

I even used student-friendly language to code the state standard into a learning target for students to easily understand. This was to make sure I covered all of the objectives to safely pass my student teaching assignment. The only expectation for the observer and the other person was to only grade me on Standards and Objectives and Presenting Instructional Content, and the structure of what we were doing today would accomplish this easily.

"Learning Target [11-12.RL.1]
- **I can** support my analysis of Chapter Nine of *The Great Gatsby*
- **By** citing evidence from Chapter Nine
- **Which is measured by** my conversations with my group members and my answers on the worksheet.
- **So that** I can use evidence to support whatever I say."

First, I began my spiel, greeting them, letting them see the bell work was already on the board, while then providing the students all of the encouragement that would help them do well and maybe give me a few bonus points. This was followed by me making sure they worked on the bell work, which was just a review question about an earlier chapter in the book. Then, as a class, we went over

194

all the learning target information. I followed this by asking questions about the material, modeling how to answer the questions (I Do). Then we did the first question on the formative assessment together to confirm if the students understood what they were doing in class (We Do). Next, I transitioned into independent practice where the students answered the questions independently or with their shoulder partner (You Do) if they needed assistance since they were already in groups and they could ask their partners, or me if there partner couldn't really help them out. I moved around the room to make sure the students did everything correctly. It was the textbook example of the *I Do, We Do, You Do*—style of teaching. When it was close to the end of class, I had the students share their answers. I then closed out with an exit ticket (the survey), and that was that.

Since I basically covered everything needed, I felt like I was in excellent shape for success. This was a textbook activity that covered all of the main points on the TAP rubric, and it was an assignment that was given to me by Mr. Saille. I was utterly relieved at how smoothly everything went throughout the class. The students did everything that was needed. Everything went well, and I was so happy that it was done.

The students left when the bell rang, and I was alone with Mr. Saille, Mr. Cichy, and the third observer.

"You need to stay here," Mr. Cichy said.

"Don't I need to go over my scores with them?" I asked, bewildered.

"No, we are going to discuss the results first, and then I will come and get you when you are done."

So, I decided to sit down in the back of the room. After all three of them left and the door closed, I was so nervous that I would do well. I did everything I was supposed to do. I just paced the entire time, reenacting the whole class period. I did everything I was supposed to do.

The standards and objectives were on the board. The learning target was coded into the appropriate language for the class. All the material was clearly designed for the students to find meaning and connection within the text. Everything was good, but I was just so nervous...

But why did I have to wait in the room by myself?

What felt like hours passed — only about two minutes (much shorter than their meeting after last week's observation), Mr. Cichy told me they were ready to see me. Walking towards the teachers' lounge, I was a death row inmate walking towards my own execution. I wonder which one of those two would push the execution button.

I enter the room. Posters adorned all three of the walls. There was a small kitchen area for all teachers to enjoy their food to my immediate right. For some reason, I never brought my own lunch. I guess the drive wouldn't be as bad if I was able to enjoy a good meal.

"Hello." I smiled while making sure I was perfectly comfortable.

"Hi. I'm Mrs. Andrea Wilson. First, I have to say did you know what you needed to do today?"

"Huh?"

"You didn't have the students do anything."

"What?"

"The only thing you did was teach them how to do a worksheet."

I was dumbfounded. I was told to give the students this assignment and how it aligned with the essential standards, and I would pass the class. So why was the observer marking me down?

"But I was told to do this by—"

"I understand that you were told to do that, but you should have made it an activity where they actually did something besides doing a worksheet."

His statement stole the words from my mouth. Betrayals are funny things, cutting deeper when they are unexpected. The heart is pierced, the blood flows freely, and the body turns grey as the life is drained away. This was how I felt from this entire ordeal. So, I just sat there and accepted that I would not pass this assessment and would be forced out of the program by the end of the week, receiving a failure in the process.

"Because your assignment was a worksheet, and you were only teaching them how to do a worksheet, I am going to give you a failing grade in Standards and Objectives. I am also going to have to fail you Presenting Instructional Content as well. Any questions?"

I was silent.

Mrs. Wilson looked over at Mr. Saille, "Is there anything else I need to do?"

"You've done everything," Mr. Saille replied.

Mrs. Wilson got up and left us alone.

"Well, that is interesting."

"But you told me to do this assignment..."

"I know, but with what she said, I am going to have to fail you. That means I will write up the report and send it over to the University."

"But you told me to do this. You even said that if I did the assignment, I would pass. Why did you lie to me? Did you do this because I brought up my TBI, and I asked to be moved from Mr. Sona's class?" My voice raised as I was pleading with Mr. Saille to not fail me. I did everything he wanted me to do, everything. I was even told I would pass the class if I did the assignment framework he gave me.

He didn't say a word.

"Why are you going to fail me?"

He never answered, and he just walked out. I didn't know what to do. How I would be able to handle this. I was afraid that I would be stuck with a $20,000+ student loan with no way to pay it back. Apparently, a student loan cannot be discharged with bankruptcy. So, I was beyond fucking screwed. My family was fucking screwed by this asshole.

I took some deep cleansing breaths to guarantee that I wouldn't let the anger flow through me. I entered a Zen-like state. I got up, left the teachers' lounge, and joined Mr. Cichy's class. I knew that I needed to go down to the Education department at *The University*. I needed to talk to them, plead with them to not allow this to really harm me. Everyone else in my cohort had already passed their student teaching assignment. I was the only one that required a fourth observation and now I will be the only one to fail.

"How did everything go?" Mr. Cichy asked, a smile itching across his face. He was almost glowing when he saw my concerned face.

"Can I please be excused?"

"Is everything alright?" He asked with mock care.

"They failed me, and I need to go down to the University to make sure everything was alright. This isn't right. I think I will need to call a lawyer too."

As I said that, Mr. Cichy's face turned into one of utter shock and concern. I didn't care. I just grabbed my stuff from the back of the room, and I left to get down to the University as soon as I could. I needed them to know how I was screwed over, how I was placed in an impossible position where I could not have passed the course. I was simply set up to fail.

As I sat in my car, I relaxed. I was away from the place that harmed me. I drove down to the University. I stopped in the education building to speak to someone who could help me. Unfortunately, the receptionist told me they would not see me today because everyone was completely booked for the day with meetings. They would call me when they had a chance.

They never did.

They sent me an email, though…

Memory before the Arizona Teachers Academy

I graduated from my community college education program. Because the University participated in a transfer pathway for community college graduates, I would have a two-year degree, and I would earn my Bachelor of Arts in Secondary Education in two more years. I would save a ton of money taking care of pointless, required courses that did nothing for my degree. I would focus all of my time just focusing on what I needed to do to get done.

But because of what was happening at the time, specifically what was going on with the Arizona Governor and their statements about public school teachers, I decided to veer away from finishing the program. So, the week before I started my Fall Semester at *The University*, I called the College of Humanities to transfer to their English program. Because most of the classes were the same, I only switched out a few of my education courses. I decided to take courses in rhetorical writing and the history of the English language. I kept the short story, novel study, and Shakespeare courses that I was originally signed up to take.

After my first semester, I realized that I couldn't just take all English courses. With the need for taking additional credits to fulfill the requirements for a bachelor's degree, I would be forced to take a minor or take a random course that suits my interest. In addition, I didn't want to waste my time earning credits in areas that would not add to my base of knowledge.

Thankfully, the College of Humanities offered a concurrent program. So, instead of declaring a minor, I could take additional courses in another field (even at another college). Because the degree I switched to was strictly about transmitting information and viewpoints to others using the English language, I decided the most helpful tool was to get a degree in Communication from the College of Social and Behavioral Sciences. The

Communication program was fantastic because I focused all my energies on rhetorical studies and how language can sway a public's viewpoint on whatever subject the rhetorician tries convincing people to follow.

If I want to be successful in the business world, I need to make sure that I can convince people what I am selling has value. I will need to even sway the people towards my beliefs based on providing information that is appropriate for their appetites.

Because most of the required English courses were already completed at the community college and a semester and a half at *The University* would finish up the rest, the vast majority of my remaining two years was focused on the communication program, especially focusing on rhetorical speaking and writing. Because I had so many credits already stashed away in English, and the major rhetorical classes I would need were already part of my planned program, I was able to throw in an extra class covering rhetoric, the digital age, gamification, and the history of video games. The course went through some areas of how different activities in life can be turned into games to increase engagement from the user. Besides breaking down the history of games and how life can be "gamified," the class also explored how video games can be tools of persuasion, allowing people to experience the trials and tribulations of another person or group of people in the comfort of their own home. In other words, it is just like watching movies, but instead of being a passive viewer — munching on popcorn, the player has a more active role, allowing them to have a more profound connection with the material.

With that in mind, in addition to my interdisciplinary training and my background studying English literature, I was overjoyed there was a pitch competition offered at *The University*. The way this competition worked is all the competitors would be interviewed by one judge individually. This was the screening round. After the screening round, the finals would have the top six entrants share their pitch to the entire panel of judges and the group. The winner of this round would get seed funding (seed funding is just money to help a startup company get off the ground).

My idea was a simple one. Because a lot of literature is in the public domain, especially information or literature appearing in the high school English and Social Studies curriculum, I pitched how my freshly created company would utilize those public domain resources to make games that would enable the students to interact with those pieces, that information. My material would allow the students to further engage the material in a way they can connect with. Since many students are primarily visual learners, this will enable a level of interaction that facilitates such lessons to become more valuable, more worthwhile. The material would take the abstract and make it tangible, real. The majority of the text would be from the classical works, but the students would be able to act on and interact with other characters within that story world. Students need to be engaged with the material to really learn from it. Why not allow those students to use their character avatar to navigate Verona of *Romeo and Juliet*, New York during F. Scott Fitzgerald's *The Great Gatsby*, or move along the frontlines during Tolstoy's *War and Peace*. Because of my idea, even though it was a fledgling one that I came up with on the fly an hour before the competition, I made it to the Final Round. I was beyond excited to give my pitch to the judges. I went over the benefits, especially from a scientific perspective.

Unfortunately for me, this simple idea was too much of a fledgling one to win. It needed to be fed, cared for by resources I did not possess as a mere college student. I finished in third place. The top two were already active businesses with customers. They just needed that extra oomph to get over the edge. I guess it wasn't such a big loss since the only thing it cost me was an afternoon, but the experience was pretty memorable. The thrill of being on stage, all the eyes on me, as I share my view of how to make the world a better place.

May 10th, 2019

This is really weird.

Yesterday, I had to attend the Convocation for the Education Program at *The University*. I was forced to sit among strangers. Everyone else from my cohort was all sitting together. They didn't talk to me, check to see how everything was going, and I couldn't face them because it sucked how I was getting screwed over. I have only one hope of being able to teach, start my new career, for the 2019/2020 school year, and that rests on a successful grade appeal. If it works out for me, I will be better able to make money when all this is done. I may have enough time to attend training before the start of the school year in August.

A few days after I filed the grade appeal, my God, I was told to come into the office and discuss the problematic events that occurred during my student teaching assignment. So, I had to go down again to the program office at *The University* to make sure everything was getting taken care of. But, unfortunately, right now, I believe they will not help me.

To make sure I followed all of the rules to properly appeal the abomination called an objective observation from the Teachers' Program, I contacted Mr. Saille about the situation and appealed the grade he gave me. During the grade appeal process to Mr. Saille, I learned he worked at MJMHS, the same as Mr. Sona. He was the school librarian. So, why did Mr. Saille force me to meet at another school? That didn't make any sense to me. Either way, during our conversation about my grade appeal, he just stated that he had already gone over my grade with me in the post-conference, and he would be unwilling to change my grade. So, that was basically a pointless step, but one that needed to be accomplished anyway.

Next, per the procedures for the grade appeal, after I contacted Mr. Saille, I escalated the situation to Dr. Vallin. Because she was an employee of *The University* and not *The School District*, I believed she would be fair to me. Furthermore, my choice of where to be educated and receive a college education would look out for me, especially in a situation like this. I paid good money for my two undergraduate degrees, Arizona paid good money for me to complete my graduate degree; so, *The University* should really be looking out for their students. That would be the most sensible thing to do. That is the most honorable thing do to do. Since I believe this place of higher education is made up of hardworking, respectable people who will look out for their own students, I shouldn't have anything to worry about at all.

I was wrong.

About two days after I filed my grade appeal directly to her, she replied how she had denied my request to change my grade based on information shared by Mr. Saille, Mr. Cichy, and Mr. Sona. As a result, I would be forced to have the Grade of E, equivalent to an F, on my collegiate record, and I would be forced to pay back the entire amount of the Arizona Teachers Academy award. Evidently, I would be the first person in the Arizona Teachers Academy's short history to fail the program and be required to repay the entire scholarship amount due to failure. Considering I was the only person who was previously disabled, I found that kind of shocking but also kind of telling about how education views people who may be labeled as differently-abled.

Mr. Vallin stated that the grade was justified because I brought up "non-school matters in front of students" when I basically complained about how I was being treated, and how I suggested that I maybe need to talk to the lawyer was not a matter to discuss in front of students, no matter what happened to me. I guess I was supposed to keep the situation quiet and behind closed doors or something — *take my beating*, if you will. I don't know why they were treating the 12th Graders who witnessed the event in high school like they were elementary-age children who couldn't understand how the world worked and how injustice could affect anyone from anywhere, especially considering some of the material the students had to read.

I wrote back to the doctor's response, explaining my feelings and what I felt was a grave injustice. I asked if there was anything I could do about the matter, and he basically referred me back to the University manual to answer my questions. I don't know why he couldn't just help me. Either way, the university manual stated that I should escalate my concern. I followed the recommendation and sent the email to Dr. Joseph Jacobs, Dean of the Teachers College. I don't know how long I will have to wait, but I hope to hear something soon. I really want to begin working as a teacher soon. Everyone else was happy about their new positions. I will still appeal the decision, and I hope for the best, but I really feel like Cyrano de Bergerac after being hit on the head with a log.

However, part of me didn't feel right with the exchange over email; so, I did something very drastic. I don't know if it will matter much, but I decided to contact the U.S. Department of Education about how I was treated. Deep down, I feel the way *The University* and *The School District* treated me should be against the law. These are places of learning, and if I am harmed because I just want to be a teacher, and I spoke up about what is clearly malice at this point, who knows how many other students are going through the same problems? I hope having an outside party look at this may help turn things in my favor.

*****

I walk out my front door at 7 AM, embracing the new day. With an infant morning stretching and yawning with the start of a new day, it brings a slight breeze that awakens the soul, revitalizes hope in my place in the world. Remembering all that I have been through, all of the problems with my own childhood, causing me to self-medicate with video games, television, and even books as a vicarious escape, an emotional release, away from each and every nail in the road. With my feet scarred from stepping on every soulless spike littering my journey, my heart fills up when I know things could have been so much worse.

Because I forgot to check the mail yesterday, I walk down my block to the mailboxes, checking to see if I received any thoughtful correspondence from my family, congratulating me on my new home. As I walk, doing such a mundane task, my hands start turning red. I also realize that I can see my breath. I guess it was a little colder than I thought, but this clean, cool air numbs all of those memories in my constantly churning brain.

I love my home.

I love my neighborhood.

I love the peace and quiet, even though the mailbox was empty.

Living in a house near a nature preserve was an excellent decision. However, I found out that sometimes a place could be too good to be true. I guess it boils down to not making sure the home was free from defects and other problems that would cause me frustration after moving in. Part of my inability to see all of the issues in a structure because I cannot see into walls. Furthermore, I didn't know or sense there was something wrong with the roof.

Sure enough, during one summer storm a year after moving into my new house, an extra heavy storm battered my home while still living in the guest room. During a monsoon maelstrom, the ceiling and the back of my house was hammered pretty extensively. This was about two weeks after the cactus fell down in front of my house, so I was used to bad things happening while I lived there. Thus I wasn't really caught by surprise by what would happen this time.

As I was playing games on the television in the living room, I began to hear the splattering of water. Consequently, I got up and investigated. In the master bedroom that I did not live in because I was too lazy to hang curtains and the shower was completely unusable because of the slightly detached shower shelf in the master bath, I saw a little bit of water dripping out of the ceiling wall that faces the backyard.

I stepped forward to see if I could put a towel and maybe a bucket underneath to save the carpet and minimize the damage. As I did so, a tear in the section of the wall near where the drip was happening opened completely up. A torrent of water begins flowing down. The ceiling, as far as I could tell, decided to share the large amount of rain that was drenched it. Once the torrent died down, I decided to get some towels and sop up the water the best I could.

Looking at the gash where the water poured out, I could say that my house was a living, breathing creature. The storm hurt it horribly, internally. I use carpet cleaner to try and scrub out the water-stained carpet. I even bring in a few fans to help dry off the house's injury, hoping to prevent mildew formation. That would definitely make this entire problem much worse. I then called my Dad and asked him to come out and help me with the roof.

Even though my Dad never graduated from high school, he was always a quick learner and a hard worker. He was one of those old school men who valued working with their hands and being street smart instead of book smart, as he would label me when I was growing up. I mean, he couldn't help me at that specific moment, but he did say he would come out and look at it when the storms died down. Then, I would just have to pick him up. He also asked me to buy him a carton of cigarettes when he is done fixing the problem with the roof.

When the time did come, he fixed it the best he could. Evidently, he did such a fantastic job that when I sold the house a few years later to move to the east side of the valley, the roofers did not see any of his handiwork. For a person that was never taught to be a roofer, I was shocked he learned how to do it just by doing it himself while working as a day laborer, doing odd jobs for different people, or working as a maintenance man for all of the complexes that we lived at.

By asking my Father to come out here and look at it, I definitely saved money. I also saved a lot of time because I didn't have to play the game of shop around for quotes. Not to say there aren't people who earned the right to charge a lot, but there are also some technicians who will demand exorbitant fees and do a piss poor job. It will then take even more money to find someone new to fix *their* mistakes while also hoping the new company isn't as bad as the first.

So, even though it wasn't the most expensive problem with my house, my Dad did save me a lot of money in the long run. In addition, the roof was repaired with little fuss on my part, and I didn't have another problem with a leaking roof. So, I guess the old saying holds true: *it is not what you know but who you know*.

May 30th, 2019

    I received an email with the decision for my appeal being escalated to the Dean of the Teachers College. My grade appeal to the Department Chair seemed to have gone nowhere. The fact the failing grade was supported due to me bringing up how I was discriminated against shouldn't have given *The University* a reason to deny my grade appeal. So, the escalation was more than warranted, but I was very anxious about what would happen. Would I be forced to continue student teaching in the Fall Semester, would I be forced out of the program, or would I end the teaching program without the ability to legally teach and have tens of thousands of dollars in grant money converted into a giant student loan?

    The decision from the education program was just sobering, and it appears like nothing more than trying to move the goalposts to support misconduct. According to Dr. Jamison, Director of School District Relation Services; Dr. Vallin, the Division Director of the Educator Preparation; and Dr. Martel, Dean of Academic Programs; I can only appeal a grade decision based on three different criteria: 1) error in grade calculation, 2) equitable grade standards because of evidence of bias/discriminatory conduct, or 3) inconsistent grading for assignments. Because I picked option two because Mr. Cichy's decided to reduce my student teaching responsibilities because of my TBI. But with the "information supplied by the Clinical Coordinator (Mr. James Saille)," *The University* concluded that the failing grade was consistent with the evidence supplied. "Even if discrimination did occur, the evidence provided by the student teacher is not enough to overturn the failing grade."

They even stated that disagreeing with the clinical coordinator was unprofessional, while my mentor teacher showed patience while dealing with someone like me. Even though I shared the emails and all the documentation that stated I was provided everything to pass the course, the committee indicated the employee from PSD was found to have consistently applied the rules. Therefore, there is no appearance of bias in the grading calculation. Furthermore, because I disclosed my traumatic brain injury, *The University* and all of their employees had the right to treat me any way they decided was appropriate, like reducing duties and responsibilities, changing assignments, or even failing to provide adequate support for a student teacher like me. Derogatory comments nor mistreatment did not outweigh the additional funding the University would receive from the Arizona Department of Education. Neither the University nor PSD employees who wrong a student teacher do not outweigh the importance of the program for providing additional funding for a place of higher learning known to swindle students out of thousands upon thousands of dollars.

Their findings can be summarized as *The University* investigated *The University* to see if *The University* or *The School District* was guilty of discriminatory misconduct regarding grading policies. *The University* found neither *The University* nor *The School District* did anything wrong. Even if it had a financial incentive for *The School District* to participate with *The University's* Teachers Program, their relationship with *The School District* was not strong enough to potentially harm fair grading, even if the individuals in question were swayed by an outside opinion or information. *The University* stated the testimony of the witnesses from *The School District* were more believable than the written correspondence or the testimony provided by the aggrieved party (me). In other words, <u>it's like the family of a murder victim finding out the killer goes free</u>

because the prosecution, judge, and jury were all friends, and the people who are supposed to bring justice were all part of the same club as the criminal.

Either way, *The University* offers me what they deem to be a panacea for my troubles. Because I had difficulty completing the material, Dr. Vallin offered to change my failing grade to an Incomplete. I can then retake a truncated student teaching experience where I will student teach from the beginning of August (when school starts) to the end of September (end of the first quarter). I will have two observations conducted by Dr. Andrew Drewsome, who works for *The University*. He was one of my former professors. The other assigned co-scorer is Dr. Nancy Smith, the college professor for one of my classes. I repeatedly requested ad nauseam for her to observe my third and fourth observations. She was unable to attend as a co-scorer for either one because of the new responsibilities required from their recent promotion within *The University*. Also, this second student teaching assignment will not have employees from the partnering school district conduct any of my assessments like the previous semester. So, I guess I am really starting to feel the results from Mr. Sona, Mr. Cichy, and Mr. Saille denying me a fair chance of graduating on time while also making me work additional time because the subjective opinions of a few prejudicial teachers are going to force me to wait longer to get employed, unlike the rest of my cohort. They are trying to recover from being one of the only universities that failed and wasted Arizona's taxpayer money and harmed a student because they spoke up and spoke out about their disability.

I know, when I did "graduate" with the rest of my cohort, all the other members of my Arizona Teachers Academy class sat together because they knew they already had teaching jobs, they already had a future in the education system. I am being forced to watch outside from the street, cold and alone. In contrast, others are deemed better because of some arbitrary reason designated by intuitions that only care about the bottom line, about how much money they can siphon from their students. At the same time, they grow fat and plump being the gatekeepers for who will succeed and who will fail, even if the criteria to designate such differences is completely suspect.

Memory before the Arizona Teachers Academy

When I compared myself to my friends, I would always become a little nervous. As far I knew at the time, my friends lacked the experiences and similar events like my younger sibling almost dying before making even the two-week-old milestone. However, this was not the real reason that we were different than other friends. Being so close to age, we developed a bond. As my brother tried to figure out the world and comprehend its meaning, my brother needed to establish a method of communication with someone willing to listen. Unfortunately, our parents did not have time for such trivial matters and left us to entertain ourselves the best we could do.

Cryptophasia, a language developed between identical or fraternal twins so they can communicate with one another before they both grasp language, occurred between my brother and me. Because I was the older sibling by one year, and I developmentally regressed with the birth of my brother, the cryptophasia was seen as a warning sign of me being developmentally disabled.

So, I was basically considered developmentally disabled because the doctors, at the time, thought I could not comprehend language with my parents and the drastic regression of my abilities (going from being potty trained to requiring diapers once again). Thus, instead of considering the language my sibling and I developed, the doctors focused on only what I lost and how I did not conform to the textbook development of the typical child. I find this to be somewhat humorous. Consequently, instead of thinking or even guessing how I was just being empathetic with my younger sibling, the doctors automatically wanted to focus on me possessing some deficit because my actions were atypical.

For some reason, it never occurred to the medical professionals or anyone else to do anything else but a quick observation and jump to a conclusion. It never occurred to them how I may be drew a connection to my struggling sibling because of the medical mistake and us being so close in age. My sibling was especially having difficulty conveying their wants and desires, so I developed a way to communicate with them. It is as if people are quick to judge something they don't understand, drawing an erroneous conclusion without having all the evidence.

I guess it makes a little bit of sense to think that I may be disabled in some way. When my baby teeth came in at around six months, the central and lateral incisors on the top row had a black line going through them. The rest of the teeth lacked enamel, requiring capping. This was a result of the medication my mother was taking while she was pregnant with me. So, the medical professionals likely assumed more severe cognitive deficits because of the dental problems combined with cryptophasia as an indication of a far-reaching disability.

Now, this was all done before they actually tried to measure my ability to learn. Eventually, a healthcare professional finally got the idea to test my overall mental abilities. As sure as the Sun will rise, I apparently performed so well on those tests that I was placed into gifted services. However, that is not the real issue. The medical professionals' disconnect from the possible cause or reason behind my conduct kept them from honestly questioning what a sibling bond may entail. This was genuinely awe-inspiring. Why would it never occur to them that I possessed a level of empathy and intelligence to form a simple form of communication? Why would they think Taylor was so damaged that such new forms of communication could never develop between both of our fledgling minds?

In a way, I understand that other people who suffered such an infliction were often in that position due to some underlining issue. I know that my mother took medication that had a real and lasting impact on the formation of my bad teeth. I realize that too much oxygen to a young brain will cause irreversible damage and result in a life knocked off the board before they could really learn to play. I know the medical professionals, being rational and educated, likely believe in Ockham's razor, or the simplest explanation is usually the right one. However, sometimes if the most straightforward seems to quick, it may be. Sometimes most inconvenient answer, the most unbelievable truth can frequently surprise the rational mind.

This is not to say that I hold medical professionals in contempt or anything. I just believe, even though we are not the paragons of fortune or the best-lived life, I have been fortunate enough to walk the fine line, stroll across the razor's edge, and do things that others think are impossible. So, to not completely offset all of the misfortune that has befallen us, maybe we have a few moments where our misfortune can be overruled by pure impossibility.

June 7th, 2019

I was just got off the phone with Mr. Steven Garth, the lawyer who works for the University, and I had to arrive early for a sit-down at 1 PM on Tuesday. They told me that I would have to come in for a meeting with the entire program to discuss my options while investigating further into my claim. Why, if I turned over the communication that showed how they treated me, would they need to investigate further? What they did has no justification. I really feel like I am being railroaded right now because *The University* just signed up an exclusive contract to send their student teachers and interns to *The School District*, especially if they are focusing on secondary education in a high school setting.

Putting the negativity and my self-doubt under mountains of self-assuredness of the truth coming to light, I was overjoyed to see the campus parking was almost empty, making a breeze because most of the other students were away, enjoying their summer break. However, because of this entire incident, because of how I was treated for bringing up my concerns about a prominent teachers union member, I was stuck here, trying to advocate for my ability to graduate so I could find a job in the 2019/2020 School Year.

I got there at 12:40.

I parked on the first level. It would be pointless and a waste of gas to move up to the second or third level. So, I parked my car in the first open spot on the bottom level, and I got out and walked towards *The University's* Education Building.

After navigating across the nearly empty abandoned areas — I saw one stray student walking out of the on-campus coffee shop — I arrived at the education building.

The grey exterior painting with sparse landscaping appears to have been untouched since the 1980s. I don't know if this is intentional or not, but it could seriously use a designer's touch.

Considering how much money the University charges for tuition, I guess the building goes untouched because it is not a big moneymaker. Economics plays a part in how a school would renovate to attract students. Since a building to train future teachers for a life in public or private education does not create employment that pays six-figure incomes, I guess they should get a pass for the building not being in the best shape.

I entered the double doors at the front of the building, and I was greeted by what appeared to be a disheveled college student. I guess summer is more laid-back and calm, lacking the hectic rush of students who try to change classes at the last second. They would likely also be there to plead because the professor is too difficult, or maybe the course is being taught more by the teacher's assistant instead of the professor themselves. The blood pressure-raising emergencies of the Fall and Spring Semesters dissipates in the Summer's heat.

"I'm here for an appointment," I said with nonchalance.

"Please take a seat. We will call you back in a moment," the receptions said to me without looking up from his papers.

I walked over to the waiting area and sat down. All the magazines were promotional material about how the life of an educator can make a big difference in the lives of students. The program advertisement played on a simple theme, the urgency of a state-wide teacher shortage and how Arizona school children were suffering from classrooms without an adequately trained educator leading them through the curriculum. Here is a sample of one of the adverts I saw on the University's website: *"The*

Students of Arizona NEEDS you to become a teacher. The University wants YOU to choose their excelling program to become a teacher that leads all other teachers. With the help of the Arizona Teachers Academy, you will graduate from the program without incurring any debt or needing to take out student loans. Instead, the program will fund each year of your degree for each year of service helping Arizona students."

Nothing like promotional irony starring me right in the face. I shouldn't be here at all. This stuff should have been taken care of with a simple email. I should have received my favorable decision and then went down to the Arizona Department of Education to get my teacher certification.

I guess this is just a formality in the process.

This should be a quick meeting because I sent over all the information, showing how I was set up to fail. I should then be told that I should have graduated and received my certificate of completion. The little piece of paper will allow me to go down to the Department of Education to obtain my teaching certificate, a certificate that will open the door for me to be employed posthaste. The promise of the Arizona Teachers' Academy providing me a pathway into education would have been my future.

The teacher shortage should have really allowed them to vote in my favor because the news already stated the drastic teacher shortage affecting all subjects in all grade levels was getting worse. So, I should be able to have employment in about two weeks. There will still be plenty of time to craft a syllabus for the upcoming 2019-2020 school year. I can plan out a rough idea of what I need to teach for the entire school year. Even though as I work through the year as I adapt and augment the curriculum to the needs of the students, I believe any extra time to predict how the students will respond will provide an opportunity to really shape the critical lessons for benchmark testing.

Instead of doing the sensible thing, the right thing, my ass is going to meet people from *The University's* Education Department. As I enter the conference room, seven people were already sitting at a collection of 10 long tables forming a rectangle that stretched across the room (kind of reminded me of the way the tables were set up at the Union meeting I was told to attend a few months prior). There were office chairs placed along the outside of the set-up. My chair, near the front, was the only unoccupied seat. I sat down near the corner where the long and short met nearest the entrance to the room.

"Hello, I am Dr. Nancy Smith. I will be one of the scorers during your next student teaching assignment." She sat alone in the middle of my long row. I requested she would be my co-scorer on both of my observations, but she refused to attend because of more important commitments.

"Hello, I'm Dr. Drewsome, and I will be the co-scorer with Dr. Smith." Considering I wanted either Dr. Smith or Dr. Drewsome to be the co-scorers during my two observations in Mr. Cichy's class, I found it a little unusual they both would now have the time to come out to where ever I will be student teaching next semester.

"Hello, I'm Dr. Michael Jamison, Director of School District Relation Services," said the gentleman sitting at the opposite corner, directly diagonal from me.

"Hello, I'm Dr. Mitchell Vallin, the Division Director of the Educator Preparation Program." He sat down next to Dr. Jamison.

"Hi, I'm Dr. Martel, Dean of Academic Programs." She was directly to my left, almost touching my right elbow.

"Hello, Mrs. Ontravios, representative of the State of Arizona Teachers Union and *The School District*. I'm here to observe." She wore a blue dress with gold trim around the color. She sat in the corner directly to my left near Dr. Martel.

"How are you doing? Mr. Garth, legal counsel for the University," stated the gentleman with blond hair, blue eyes. He wore a grey suit, light blue shirt, and a grey tie with tiny blue horses, *The University's* mascot, all over it. He sat in the long row closest to Dr. Jamison.

"I'm doing okay," I said while looking at all the faces staring at me, analyzing what I was doing and how I was acting.

"Before we begin," Dr. Vallin stated. "We need to sign a paper about why you will need more time to complete your student teaching experience."

"Okay."

"Before you sign this form to allow your continuation as a student teacher, we need to discuss what was stated by your former mentor teacher. According to Mr. Cichy, the reason you were removed from your student teaching was because of your inappropriate behavior against students. As a result, they felt you were a danger to them, and they asked for you to be removed." Dr. Vallin gave out a sigh. I was filled with concern because this was completely different than what happened.

"What?"

"Can you tell us what happened?" Mr. Garth interjected.

"Uh, well. Nothing like that. After my observation. Mr. Saille, Mr. Cichy, and the second observer went into the teachers' lounge. I was told to wait until Mr. Cichy returned, which seemed kind of strange. Even though I was supposed to be there for the entire feedback session, they made me wait around for like fifteen minutes. When Mr. Cichy came back, I went in there. When I sat down, the observer...uhh..."

"Mrs. Wilson," said Dr. Vallin.

"Mrs. Wilson? I asked repeatedly, and they would never give her name. So anyway, when I sat down, she basically said that 'you just taught students how to do a worksheet.' I told her that Mr. Saille had given me the information and said I would pass if I used that assignment. But Mrs. Wilson didn't care. She said that he would not pass me, and then Mr. Saille excused her. After the observer was gone, Mr. Saille started going over my scores, and I kept saying that I did exactly what he told me to do, everything. He even promised me if I did Dissecting Gatsby assignment, I would pass the course. He kept deflecting my appeals, and I was like, 'you told me! Why did you lie to me?' At that point, he said that he couldn't talk to me because I was so upset, and he left."

Mrs. Ontravios just sat there, watching. Evidently, her poker face was tremendous because I didn't know if she agreed with me or she was siding with what Mr. Saille did. So even though Mr. Saille was a member of the same Teachers Union, she would be able to see that my treatment was even close to being remotely fair.

"What happened when you went back to Mr. Cichy's room?" asked Dr. Martel.

"Well, I was upset. I asked to be excused so I could go down to the University to talk with you. Mr. Cichy, with a smirk on his face, asked what was wrong, and I told him that I needed to go back to the school to talk to the University. I even said that I may call a lawyer because of what happened. When I uttered lawyer, Mr. Cichy acted shocked and began acting like I said something completely obscene. But I was too focused on getting to the University to talk with Dr. Vallin about what happened."

"Did you say anything else?" Mr. Garth asked.

"No. I did not. So, that account that you just read to me is completely inaccurate. None of that happened."

"What do you want it to say?" Dr. Vallin asked.

"Everything I just told you," I answered.

All of them looked at each other. The pause in the conversation was unusual, unsettling. Was this one of those moments of awkward silence that goes along with every exchange, or were they trying to find the right words to give me?

"Well," I started, "I will sign the form when it accounts for exactly what happened. I will not sign anything that says I did not conduct myself in anything less than professional behavior. That is objectively false. Anything that says I don't know how to conduct myself is false, and I will never support dishonesty among anyone, even my own students."

"We will get back to you," answered Dr. Martel.

It is Friday, and *The University* hasn't emailed or called me back.

Memory before the Arizona Teachers Academy

When my family lived out of hotels, there was one enormous benefit for this decision. We had access to a pool to swim and enjoy ourselves. Of course, the quality of the swimming pools would differ, but I was comforted by the knowledge that I would have access to one, allowing me to rinse away any problems. Also, the best pools at the best hotels would have a slightly bluish-tint to their crystal clear water (reflection of the blue sky), whereas the worst ones were cloudy and with a sickly off-green tint. In the case of the swimming pool at this hotel, it was evident that this wasn't the best pool available. The owners of the hotel were probably not adding as much chlorine to the water as recommended or required to keep the guests from getting sick.

Besides the visible problems with the pool water, another problem with this pool was the deck. Apparently, the designers for the hotel decided to mix little tiny rocks into the concrete. Most of the deck was this lighter brown in color that matched the sand surrounding the entire pool. I believe the pool installers used the rough, sharp, green stones to save on cost and minimize the risk of someone slipping on the pool deck. The idea was to give the residents a little more grip when they walked upon a soaked deck. It would also encourage the residents to get into the water instead of loitering around the pool. Fewer problems would be bound to happen if people played around in the water instead of horseplay on the dangerous deck. All of this boiled down to discomfort for the sake of safety.

In my case while staying at the hotel, I learned to dislike any pool visitation when it did not involve going into the pool. So, when we played tag or whatever in the pool, it would remain confined to that area throughout the entire duration of the activity. Thus, the pathway to play and enjoyment in the pool always involved the water.

However, there was one time that it was not the case. This pair of older kids (I think they were in 7th Grade) would try and run us off almost every opportunity they could. I guess I would label them as bullies. They were identical twins. Both had blond hair, blue eyes and were covered in freckles. They likely outweighed us by about 50 pounds or so.

Anyway, no matter what we were doing at the time, these jerks would try and ruin our fun. They would do whatever it would take to get us out of the pool and allow themselves to enjoy it all by themselves. They would splash us incessantly, dunk us, punch us, and do whatever it would take to accomplish their goal. Without parents to really supervise or regulate the pool—"parental supervision is required"—and my Dad was at work, and my mom was asleep on her bed, we were left to fend for ourselves.

So, my sibling and I were in the water, pretending to be undersea explorers, diving down deep in the murky water to find dangerous, alien things. The time was flying as we were having fun, uncovering ancient mysteries from long ago.

The two older kids happened to be were walking by, and they saw us.

"Hey, what you guys doing?"

"Uh, we are just exploring this undersea wreckage," I yelled back with my childhood confidence.

"Awesome. Can we play?"

"Yes!" Taylor's reply showed how we were both tired of our metaphorical tiny, deserted island for ourselves. These were the first kids who wanted to play with us since we moved to Van Buren months ago. Even though they bullied us in the past, maybe things would change for the better this time.

The other kids went to their rooms.

My sibling and I continued to play. Wreckages from long ago were just within our grasp. Translucent monsters allowed us to see their last meals; carnivorous creatures who would pull out undersea tables to elegantly dine on their helpless prey; gigantic peaceful ruination of ancient civilizations were keeping us company while we waited.

When we gave up any hope the older kids would come back and play, the two arrived. One was wearing white basketball shorts and a black shirt, while their friend was wearing black basketball shorts and a white shirt. A section of a chest board became two living people, and they would join our game.

"What game are we going to play first?" The pair's leader had long brownish hair, blue eyes, and freckles that dotted their tanned skin.

"Well, it looks like they are just swimming," the other one said. "So, I think we can play a better game…" The other's greenish-brown eyes showed a particular delight on their blemish-free tanned skin. Their black hair was pulled back into a ponytail, showering care for appearance the leader did not. "…Tag would be way more fun."

"Uh. The pool deck has little rocks in it." I said with an air of concern. "If one of us slips, it would really hurt. Also, the rocks hurt my feet when I get outta the water."

"We will just play in here." The brownish-hair teenager replied. "You can trust us. Nothing is gonna go wrong."

We played around for about twenty minutes, everyone was having fun. Unfortunately, my sibling was a little slower when they swam, so Taylor would always wound up getting caught. However, they would eventually corner one of us, and that is how Taylor would get out of just being it for the rest of the game.

When the brown-haired teenager was trying to avoid Taylor, the kid started to run up the pool steps to get out of the water—a clear violation of the rules. My sibling,

225

not allowing the prey to get away, quickly tagged the brown-haired kid on their left foot as they were getting out.

Before Taylor could confirm the tag, the black-haired kid quickly stated, "that wasn't a tag! You missed."

"What?" I said. "That was clearly a tag. Their leg moved and everything. Don't cheat!"

"That wasn't a tag!" said the brown-haired kid.

"It was!" Taylor shouted and celebrated his triumph of not-being-it.

"Yeah, I saw it!" I egged on, showing support for my sibling.

"No!" said the brown-haired kid with a shove. Taylor slipped on the pool bottom and was submerged for a moment. Then, the black-hair kid pounced and tried to keep Taylor underwater.

I jumped on the back of the black-haired kid. The intention was to pull the kid off so Taylor could breathe.

As I was in the process of breaking up the escalation of the game, a white flash filled my field of vision. A sharp pain shot through the back of my skull traveled along the nerve endings in my head and neck, and I fell forward. My body broke up the dunking altercation.

"Hey," Taylor yelled back. "What are you doing?"

"Just playing," said the aggressor. "We are playing boxing now."

I came to my senses, the pain still lingered, but I was trying to escape any further damage. I got out of the pool and started to grab my towel. I looked up as I reached out and grabbed my belongings, and I saw the brown-haired kid decided one shot was not good enough and started advancing on me.

The brown-haired kid started running towards me, fist pulled back for another shot, and I began to run. The pain in my feet from the entire rocks was unimportant at that very moment. I did not want to get into a fight, especially since we were just having fun. We just came here to swim.

I made a half-lap around the pool.

I slipped.

The entire left side of my body (arms, legs, torso, and shoulder) was grated like cheese. I yelled out in pain as my nerves screamed to me the extent of the damage.

I started to run.

Out of the pool.

Down the sidewalk.

Into the hotel room at the very end of the building—about 150 yards away. This was the usual way for my body to deal with a situation like this.

I ran into the room, jumped on the bed, and kicked my legs to calm myself down. The pain subsided. It washed away. Something replaced every painful tingle. Adrenaline, endorphins allowed a moment of calm. Unfortunately for the bullies, with that calmness came anger.

The anger from what those kids did to me exploded with a massive torrent. I stopped crying. The chlorine and tears stopped mixing in a clash of joy and pain.

I started to run back towards the pool. The blood from injury streaming down my legs, my side, my arms. It didn't matter. I was going back.

I entered the pool area.

The brown-haired kid was near the ladder located in the deep side of the pool. Seeing me, both kids started to laugh at me, called me a *little baby*.

I walked to the section of the pool, directly over the kid who laughed at me. The black-haired kid pointed at me and started to pantomime the universal crying gesture.

Without a word, I jumped into the pool.

Not into a place directly next to or near the brown-haired kid. No, I jumped directly onto the kid. Then, as I did, I kicked down onto both of their shoulders.

As the rest of my body crashed into the water, satisfaction began to emerge from deep within my core. It washed away the pain, the betrayal, the deceit we experienced from these assholes. They never bothered with us, talked with us, or even looked our way the rest of the time we lived in that hotel.

July 8th, 2019

 Well, I wanted to start working and earn my degree at the same time, so I am going to start calling all the schools out here. I am still waiting to get a call back for an actual interview out here. I have been to five different teacher job fairs, I have applied for over 60 jobs, and I am not getting any serious traction. It seriously feels like there is not really a teacher shortage. Every time I go to a job fair, I see a line of people trying to score their first position. Actually, I have seen a few instances where these young people, about seven years younger, getting offered a teaching job on the spot. Was the entire program a lie? I really feel like the promises that came to me, a job waiting for me when I was done with the program, was nothing more than a concoction from the Teacher Union's PR Department.

 I would always follow up a few days after I submitted my application for employment, even leaving a message with the appropriate party conducting the interviews at the school. The secretary would say they would take down my number and call me when they closed the applications, making it a fair process for all of those involved. But even after that statement, even after the promise, none of the schools in desperate need of teachers will even give me an interview. From the 60 applications, I scored only three interviews. *THREE!*

 During all three interviews, the administration at whatever school decided to interview me would just say they would need to conduct the interview over the phone because of staffing concerns. Not in person. No. Over the damn phone. I lived in the STATE! It wasn't like I couldn't just drive out there. If I was going to teach at a school, everyone involved should damn well be comfortable with my commute. I should be able to get in my car, drive out there, and be ready to do my job, right? Hell, I knew teachers already at the district that lived farther than me, and they had no problem getting a job. They would show up about two hours before the ringing of the first bell because it would allow them to catch up on the previous day's lesson. So, I could never understand why I was not getting any opportunity to teach out there.

What was the holdup? Didn't the *Red for Ed* movement tell all of us there was a teacher shortage, right? So I guess I shouldn't have said anything against a member of the Teachers Union. I really think I am being ostracized out here because I wouldn't let those teachers abuse me...

For comparison's sake, I put in a general application in Baltimore County, MD, and I had over 30 interview requests, even though I did not live in Maryland. Each of the 30 interviews boiled down to conference calls with me and three other individuals (usually the Principal, the Department Chair, and another teacher within the Department). Instead of following a script like the other Arizona schools, they would ask me questions about how I would assist the overall program, what a typical lesson plan would look like, my academic goals for a class, and how I would see myself giving back to the community. These interviews would go well, but it would always derail when I would talk about how soon I would be moving out there. If I was in the position that I could just uproot my family, I would move out to Maryland in a heartbeat.

I was all for moving to another state to teach until I realized the implications of such a move. The entire point of moving me out of the state would be to get me running away from those who wronged me, who harmed me, and who would do whatever they could to promote their false narrative on how I was a lousy teacher. Out here, I honestly believe they are no different than any other bullies out there, chasing me along the pool deck.

So, I will keep my hopes up. I will keep fighting for what is right. But, when all is said and done, I hope the powers-that-be at *The University* sides with me. The evidence is as plain as day. There wouldn't be a logical reason for them to side with *The School District*, right? *The University* was more than happy to take my money, so I believe they would represent me with fairness and respect, befitting their alumni. So, with the evidence being as plain as day, the changing testimony from Mr. Cichy and the email correspondence between Mr. Saille and myself when I sent him a follow-up email confirming what we discussed in the big meeting in January at the start of the semester, there would be no reason for the University to go against me, especially since I am providing a written account of the entire incident. Also, I haven't heard anything about my concerns from the U.S. Department of Education. I haven't received a phone call, or even a letter regarding my situation. I guess the government moves slowly; so, I will just have to wait to hear back.

I also just realized something. I think the only reason Mr. Sona invited me to the Union meeting my last week in his class was for other Union members to identify me as an undesirable. So, I made up my mind to file a complaint with the National Labor Relations Board.

Hopefully, they can help me as well.

Memory before the Arizona Teachers Academy

We were upstairs at the townhouse apartment where Michael, our cousin, lived. Unfortunately, the deep brown outside did not match the white walls with red floorboards with slightly off-green carpet on every floor. I don't know who picked the colors, but I can safely say that it was very hideous.

Because it was a townhouse apartment, there were two sets of four buildings with four two-story units each (accompanied by a twelve foot by twelve foot backyard for each unit), one set on each side of the covered parking lot. Along each side of the parking lot, both sidewalks traveled the length of the complex, ending with a large office building, workout center, and swimming pool area. The sidewalk was long, worn, and cracked at a few points by the intense heat of the summer sun. The green two feet by two feet shrubs planted on regular intervals of every three feet (with a sprinkler head between each shrub) were an attempt to distract from the monotony of the overall surroundings. Combined with the giant lined bush that encircled the outside of the property, the designers attempted to make the place as appealing to potential renters as possible.

Now, I imagine that planting these cheap bushes would have an almost comical result for late-night eyewitnesses. If a person wasn't mindful, especially walking in a drunken stupor home from a party, I could imagine them tripping over and crashing into bushes. I wonder how many times this occurred? Well, it wasn't that important because I was way too young to drink. Also, my memory of beer tasting like what I would imagine horse piss to taste like was still a little reminder a constant reminder to me not to drink ever again. I think that is why my Dad gave me some. When he told me to remember that taste, I guess he attempted to ingrain the displeasure firmly within my mind. The idea was if beer tasted nasty to a kid, the child would definitely remember how bad it tasted as an adult, and they would avoid drinking it.

Either way, I tried to spend the night at my cousin's house. The idea, the concept behind the arrangement was supposed to look like this: we would just enjoy ourselves, play video games, conquer extremely challenging 8-bit bosses, and have an overall increase of enjoyment that was not matched at home. The time hanging out with our cousin was supposed to be a small respite, even though it was only across the street. Any slight change appeared to be a marked improvement over the dysfunction at home.

It was about seven at night when I heard the door open. I paid no mind to the door because, ya know, we were kids. About five minutes after hearing someone was at the door, I saw my mom open Michael's bedroom door. Behind Mom, I saw Michael's mother standing, looking very concerned. What was going on? Why was my mom here? Was everything alright?

"You need to come home," my mom said with the care and concern she showed me.

Michael's mother quickly interjected, "That's for the best."

"What's going on, Mom?" Michael's curiosity allowed him to ask the questions that I was too afraid to blurt out. I mean, if my mom came out here, it had to be very serious, considering Michael's mother came up and was standing at the entrance to Michael's door.

"Just turn off the game. Your cousin needs to leave." I was stunned by the statement. What happened? What could have happened that would have turned the day on its head so quickly?

"FINE! Cuz, see ya later."

"No. That ain't happening." The concern of his mother quickly turned to anger. What happened? Why was there a sudden change?

I, being the shy one, didn't say anything. I just packed up my stuff (my blanket, my pillow), and I started to exit the room. I walked down the stairs to the front door, a slow procession from our plans for the night.

The crisp, cool night showered me with the sparkles of stars light-years away — a stark contrast to what just occurred in my Mike's house. There was a slight bit of wind in the air, washing away the negativity of being thrown out of my cousin's house.

As my mom exited the house a moment after me, the door slammed shut. I continued to walk across the complex, down the sidewalk, towards a home that was more warzone than a habitable place to live.

"I have to tell you something," my mom, with the hint of sadness in her voice, was an attempt to calm my frayed nerves and hurt feelings. "I got a call from the doctor."

"Uh, okay?"

"The doctor said you were positive for Hepatitis B."

"What's Hepatitis B?"

"It is a liver disease."

"Then why was I sent home?"

"Well, Mike's mom said she had Hepatitis C."

"Huh?"

"She didn't want him to get exposed to the virus. She had enough problems already, and she didn't want him to get sick."

"Okay…"

From then on, we became effectively outcasts from the community, plus I wasn't allowed to see my cousin anymore. Thankfully, a month later, my parents decided to move to a new complex off of Townley. New school, unique experience, and the knowledge that I shouldn't let Mom share any personal information about us because it could be very harmful.

October 21st, 2019

Mr. Marcus reached out to me a few days after finishing my short, abbreviated student teaching assignment at Eden High School in Scottsdale, AZ. So, I was hoping my situation had actually improved since the last time I met with anyone. Well, I had to travel down to *The University* today to meet with the lawyer hired by the school to help field my complaint, especially since I escalated the concern to the Disability Resource Center.

Looking back to my previous experience, the last time I met before my last placement, we had the meeting in a large conference room with about seven people from the Teachers College. So, this meeting being smaller, less crowded was very different, if not a little off-putting. It was really uncomfortable just having to meet with one person and discuss how I was treated during my student teaching assignment.

After I arrived, checked in with the receptionist at the front of the building, I was escorted to a conference room where Mr. Marcus was sitting at the table with a legal pad and a stack of documents. We went over information that I needed to sign that included lies that were shared by Mr. Cichy. They wanted me to admit that I even physically assaulted a student. I said, "I will not sign anything unless it has an accurate account of what happened."

So, I never even signed that supposedly important paper. I don't know why they want me to admit to something I didn't do. I explained how everything was a lie on that paper, but they still refused to change or even augment their report in any way to contain the truth of what really happened. They always want me to admit that I was physically abusive to the students, which is beyond illogical. Either way, the meeting with Mr. Marcus was basically the same song and dance, over and over and over again. Mr. Marcus was trying to get me to sign some form with the same lie on it, and I refused to sign. He then asked me a few questions, and I went about my day. Don't they have a different tune?

Are they trying to get me to sign this paper so they can recoup the $20,000 for a degree that has not even been conferred yet? I believe the combined total of how much the state and I had paid for my education was over $40,000; so, I could not understand why *The University* was being so difficult, trying to promote a false narrative shared by the people of *The School District* where I had my problematic student teaching experience with a bunch of bigots. Either way, I will do what my Dad told me and never admit to something I didn't do. But, if I did, Dad would say I better take my lickings because someone's word is what matters.

"If you don't have your word, you don't have anything."

Now, there is something that seems unusual that I failed to mention. When I participated in this second student teaching assignment, I was told I would get my Letter of Completion as soon as I passed student teaching. This would mean I could get my teaching license right away since I had already passed both of the Arizona Educator Proficiency Examinations for "Professional Knowledge: Secondary Education (NT052)" and the "English Language Arts (NT301)" to become an educator. Actually, I had to pass the NT052 just to get into the Arizona Teachers Academy.

So, after I completed the requirements, when I asked them to uphold their promise, I was told by Dr. Vallin that I needed to wait until the December 15th Convocation to receive the letter, which I found extremely odd. They told me I had to wait due to the University's policy of only graduating students at the end of the Fall or Spring Semesters. Considering everyone else in my cohort received their letters at the end of June, which was not the end of the Fall or Spring Semester, I wonder why they delayed my chance to get into the classroom.

Memory before the Arizona Teachers Academy

A minor imperfection in the dam, starting as intermittent drops, increases as the edges erode away, growing larger, expanding to a torrent, flooding the valley, washing away the human hubris. I was lying on my bed in my one-bedroom apartment. It was about three months since I was released from the hospital. I watched a detective show, and the episode was about a criminal who suffered from dementia due to an untreated illness.

Even after learning how my life was ultimately changed, that did not break me. The moment was simpler, more detached. A pressure of every moment and perceived injustice reached a focal point, a point where breaking down was the only release. In the last scene in show, the killer is in a mental institution, he is being cradled like a small child by his wife because his brain was damaged beyond repair. At that moment, everything rushed out of me. Every pain, discomfort, abandonment, the emptiness of a room occupied by only one streamed down my face between uncontrollable sobs, snot welling up, and running from my nose. If crying cleanses the soul, the conceptualization of my spiritual torrent should have been nothing less than a paragon. And I laid back, between intermittent sobs and attempt to relax, and looked at a ceiling that was dirty for goodness knows how long, in an apartment where luxury was considered a moment without loud music from downstairs, causing roaches to flee in terror.

I fixated on what was going in during conversation between lover/murder, care/destruction, hope/hopelessness. The episode involved a person who contracted syphilis. Because it went undiagnosed and was untreated for decades, the patient was in the tertiary stage. As she held her husband, the vacant stare in his eyes, the childlike reaction to the love of his life, that is what caused me to cry. Now, this cry was not a small tear or two. No, it was a total breakdown into a wail regarding my misfortune.

Was this my future?

Even when I watched the 2007 Documentary *Coma*, I did not cry. I guess the reason was I emotionally kept myself disconnected from the entire experience. Even when the young man died, it did not affect me in the same way as that damn TV show. I guess I did not go into the show expecting to see my worst fears right on the screen, a glimpse of what may likely happen. Instead, I knew in my heart that I would need to press forward whenever I got the chance. Time, after all, slowly walks behind, knife in hand, to plunge the corrupt blade deep into the spine, cutting out the spark, lowering the curtain on a solo performance.

January 10th, 2020

This week, after I put in my application for an opening at *The School District* for a position at Michael Joseph Mansfield High School because I just wanted to take a chance of getting a job, even if it was at the place that treated me so poorly, I still really need a job. Even though it ended on a sour note, I think I will be treated differently if I get a chance to work there. But, then, all the problems would just be water under the bridge. Life is way too short to hold grudges. I know I placed other applications through, and I never heard anything, but I felt things would be different this time.

I was caught by surprise when I received an email from Mr. Charles Isaac, the Office Secretary at MJMHS, about my interview opportunity in front of a panel on Tuesday. Even though they gave me less than 24-hours to really prepare, I guess it may work out. Mr. Isaac told me that I would have a full panel, and everything would be set up for a virtual interview.

I did find it a bit odd that they would only allow me to interview virtually. By denying me an opportunity to interview in person, I could not show the interviewers my complete portfolio or use examples of how I managed classroom climate. After all, I need to show them I can keep students on task if I hope to teach for a public school. But with a denial of the opportunity to really show my skills, I rationalized how I would need to use my words to convey the interview panel. So I accepted the chance of gaining my first teaching job and prepared the best I could that night and the morning right before the interview.

Tuesday morning, I received the email providing the link to the virtual conference. I felt terrific about this opportunity. I knew I would be able to get a contract sometime later in the week. I had everything set up in my room for a fantastic interview. I looked online for resources to help me plan and I mapped out all he potential questions they would ask me. I would really wow them with my care and concern. I would even tell them my own story about everything I overcame to get to this moment and why I would be the best and ideal candidate for the position.

I mean, how could they not accept someone who pulled themselves up, proving all the medical professionals wrong, showing them how not all brain injuries are the same? Some people can and do thrive after such wake-up calls. If athletes can suffer severe brain injuries and still put up record numbers, why couldn't I be the paragon of virtue for my own students? I came, I saw, I conquered. I think students will like a teacher who is a bit inspirational and even shares some of the same experiences.

I couldn't have been more wrong.

Because I was applying for an English teaching position at MJMHS, the standard procedure is for a teacher to be interviewed by a panel of the school principal, a curriculum director, a master teacher, and other staff members like an assistant principal. So, unsurprisingly, I was expecting this when I logged into the session.

Unfortunately for me, I found that it fell far below my expectations. Considering I was interviewing for an English teaching position, I was expecting to be interviewed by at least four people from the Administration and the English Department. Unfortunately, this was not the case. The people who made up my virtual interview were Veronica Mason, Assistant Principal; Andrea Samson, an algebra teacher and a member of the teachers union; and Michelle Olsen, a special education teacher and a union member. I saw both teachers sitting next to Mr. Sona at that union meeting I was pressured into attending last year.

"Hello, welcome to your interview," said Ms. Mason. "Let's introduce ourselves. I'm Ms. Veronica Mason, and I will be conducting your interview."

"I'm Andrea Samson, and I represent the Union."

"I'm Michelle Olsen, and I'm just observing."

My heart sank as I realized that this was not an actual interview. It was just a sham. The only reason the school gave me an *interview* was to probably protect themselves legally. They had no intention of ever hiring me. I guess it makes sense. After all, I pissed off one of their Union members, making them look bad because I voiced my concerns about mistreatment.

So, I went through the motion, answering all of the questions in a very detail-oriented fashion. First, I would bring up a scenario from my own experience as a student teacher and a substitute that directly relates to the question; second, I would then offer a solution to the problem in a step-by-step manner that would explain how my process would solve the problem; and finally, I would say how it was successful and to what extent. Even though they were my experiences from the classroom, my methodical planning made it feel like a textbook example of how to have a successful teacher interview.

Unfortunately, the interviewer and the two union representatives did not feel the same, or they could not feel the same because of my prior history with Mr. Sona. They probably labeled me as a troublemaker who would not sit down and just accept systemic inequities against people with disabilities. So, even though I had no hope of ever getting the job, I smiled and thanked them for their time.

Yesterday, I received confirmation that I did not get the position because another candidate was offered the position and accepted. So, I guess I can chalk the experience up to practicing my interview skills for maybe getting another job somewhere. However, I am a little worried if I don't get a job soon, I might have to pay back the entire loan. If that is the case, I don't know what I will be able to do.

Memory before the Arizona Teachers Academy

Planning to move from Florida to California, my whole family loaded ourselves up into a station wagon. The idea of moving out there was to be closer to our grandparents who already had a nice little place of their own. In addition, my father believed it would give us a fresh start with a change of scenery. The only problem was driving all the way from Pinellas Park to Marina Del Rey, a grueling trip of over 2,500 miles.

It might have been more problematic sitting up for hours upon hours to get there for my parents. For my sibling and me, we did not have the benefit of cellphones or other modern technology to make the time fly, but we did have the comfort of a bunch of clothes in trash bags that could be used as cushions or pillows. But considering all of the clothes were still dirty, there was the faint scent of unwashed and mildew that robbed me of any comfort. Nevertheless, Taylor didn't seem to have any problem with the arrangement.

Even with the cushion of spoiled, dirty clothes, my racing mind could not find any form of relaxation. I couldn't read because I would get motion sickness, and the risk of me throwing up all over the backseat was not worth the risk. I mean, we had all of our belongings stuffed into an old station wagon, and I don't think my family would appreciate all of their clothes being stained by my puke.

Looking at the moving landscape as we sped down the highway, admiring the changing scenery, relaxing as the bountiful green of wetlands and forests transitioned into the grassy terrain of the Midwest before transforming into the lightest brown upon light brown upon dark brown speckled with green. I was shocked about everything because it was so different than the endless green of Florida.

When we made a rest stop somewhere in New Mexico, I saw a few bats flying around at dusk. I never saw one before. It was crazy seeing little rodents flying around, aiming for the bugs that circle around the street lamps. Heck, Taylor and I even got to see one that was dead on the ground. Because I was squeamish and cautious about what would kill one of those flying creatures, neither one of us took a chance to touch one of them. With the information I know now about rabies and its 99.9% mortality rate, I am glad I had enough sense not to do something foolish.

Either way, our journey continued along the winding, boring highways of the Southern United States. Unfortunately, our parents didn't discuss where we were really going or where we would stop and rest because of our age. Looking back to that time, I know my parents only told us what we needed to know to protect us because everything surrounding the move was well above my age scale. However, even with my young mind, I hoped they would eventually give us a little bit of information that would help us understand why we were traveling west.

During our trip, this was the first time I had ever learned that my mom grew up spent several years in Phoenix, Arizona. She didn't really go into detail about how it treated her, but I guess it was a place she really enjoyed. Actually, since we entered Arizona in early October, the climate was not even a bit hostile.

Even though she spent many of her formative years in Phoenix, we stopped at her sister's house in New River. She and her husband lived in a lovely two-story ranch-style house. It was nice and quiet. Even though St. Pete was not loud, this was even more removed from nature. My Aunt and Uncle did not even own a television. For them, they just liked to enjoy the relaxation of nature while the rest of the world went on its merry way. So, it was nice and all, but we still had to make it out to California.

But little did I know, Arizona would become home, and I would be a high school graduate before ever getting the chance to visit the Golden State.

February 26th, 2020

Today, I had a meeting with Dr. Michelle Indea, the Vice Provost of *The University*. She was supposed to go over everything regarding the incident during my student teaching last year, but she was not alone. A person in a suit and jacket sat next to Dr. Indea. I was not expecting two people to be a part of the meeting, especially for a discussion about my complaint. This seemed like something wasn't right because I wasn't expecting another person to be in her office, but I just went with it.

With the information that I provided, information revealing the extent of the misconduct of the PSD employees, the investigation must be coming to an end, and I believe there will be justice for the wrongs that were perpetrated against me — and to an extent, my family. Thankfully, *The University's* Disability Resource Center is investigating my claim, but I don't know. Why would someone else be here?

"Hello. I'm glad you could make it," Dr. Indea said with a smile. "Because your case was too large, too complex for the Disability Resource Center, we asked Mr. James Bevel, Esq. to help make sure that we are not leaving any stone unturned."

I was blindsided by *The University* and DRC bringing in assistance from the outside to help with an investigation by an outside party. Why would *The University* hire an outside law firm to assist them in their investigation of wrongdoing by teachers at PSD? I've heard that such an action is to make sure they protect themselves from potential liability, but they could also be about trying to uncover the truth. With the conduct by Mr. Sona, Mr. Cichy, and Mr. Saille being a shockingly apparent attempt to undermine the intent of the Arizona Teachers Academy, I guess this is just a thorough investigation.

Mr. Bevel, with a slight smile, asked, "Do you have any written communication of what occurred between you and employees from *The School District*?" Mr. Bevel asked.

"Well, Mr. Saille received and responded to the emails that I sent explaining my traumatic brain injury. Here is the letter where I first told Mr. Saille that I am a traumatic brain injury survivor. He didn't respond after sharing the information, even though this email is part of a long email chain with back and forth communication. In the information I already sent, he confirms that he knows about my traumatic brain injury. There was also communication when he gave me the "Dissecting Gatsby" assignment and stated I would pass my student teaching if I used the assignment. Finally, I provided all of the Positive Feedback from Mr. Sona and Mr. Cichy that they uploaded into the system.

"If you look at the date stamp on the last positive feedback, then look at the date of the email when I explained to Mr. Saille how Mr. Sona made me uncomfortable with his disparaging remarks about me and my ability to perform as a teacher with a TBI. After that, there was no more feedback for almost a month, only on my last day in his classroom.

"On my last day at the site, the last day in Mr. Sona's classroom, he gave me one last bit of feedback, making stuff up about how I treated the students. Then, when I returned to Mr. Cichy's class, he would only give me negative feedback the entire second time I was in his classroom. The only time non-negative feedback was given was during the district testing period. To further compound the problem, Mr. Cichy also left out that he would only allow me to teach his 11th Grade class that he took on because the other teacher quit or left. So, for five hours, he just had me sitting in the back, yell at me for sitting in the back, and then when I started to move around the classroom, he would yell at me to go to the back to my little nook.

"Look at the two observers that came to my last two observations. The first person, I never heard of him, but he gave me basically the same scores that I received previously, stating that I did not grow in any way. I guess he was some teacher when I looked him up, but I wish I had written down his information to provide it, but since he was brought in by *The University*, you guys should have the information already. When I took the chance to look her up, the other observer Andrea Wilson was actually in the Oregon newspaper and had a few articles written about how she was one of the people tied to a corruption lawsuit for *misappropriating* education funds. She is the one that gave me two 1's for my observation. She even stated that I did not teach the students at all. Besides not even documenting the state standard that was clearly on the board and on my presentation slides, Mrs. Wilson said I was just teaching the students how to do a worksheet, even though assessing and connecting previously taught material is one of the most important parts of the job."

"Did you tell anyone about this?" Mr. Bevel inquired.

"Well, I called the Program Manager at *The University*. She told me everything will work out, even if it makes you uncomfortable. It also did not matter what Mrs. Wilson was accused of doing at a previous school. I asked to be moved, and *The University's* Education Department was accommodating me by sending in the second scorer."

"Okay."

"Prior to me signing off to going to whatever school they could find me, Dr. Martin, Director of the Student Placement, told me that if I fail the course, I will have to pay back the entire loan. So, they were going to transfer me back to my old school, bring in some observers to make sure Mr. Saille wasn't missing anything, and everything would be fine; so, I didn't really think anything about it until my last observation appeared to be something to force me out of the program.

"When I brought up about them knowing my health history and their inaction to make sure I was not abused, they told me to do another student teaching assignment at a school district near my house. This time, it would only have to be eight weeks. After that, I would get my Letter of Completion to receive my teacher certification in September and get any teaching job.

"Unfortunately, after I completed the program, they told me that I had to wait until December 15th because I would not technically graduate the program, and they only hold graduation ceremonies in May or December, but that seemed pretty damn odd—considering the rest of my cohort received their letters in July.

"So, I had to wait two extra months, and I could not find a teaching position *ANYWHERE*. I was told that schools don't have openings mid-year, even though I saw multiple openings at a bunch of different school districts—none of which gave me a callback.

"It was so bad that when I went to a job fair at a school district, during a panel interview with multiple schools that had English openings, I mentioned that Mr. Sona was my former student teacher mentor. I even explained how it was funny that Mr. Sona would initially be my intern mentor when I originally was working towards an undergraduate degree in secondary education — before switching majors and getting my two BAs.

"Well, the panel had me wait in the hall for about 25 minutes while they deliberated if they could offer me a contract. Awkwardly, one of the panelists came out and mentioned that they could not offer me a job for their school district.

"So, I communicated my frustration to the Dean of the Teachers College, and she forgave my Grant program— which kind of eases the burden, but now I cannot find a job as a teacher. Have I been ostracized for bringing up my concerns?"

Dr. Indea leaned over to the lawyer and whispered something. Mr. Bevel just nodded as he locked at me.

"Well, I am not in a position to say the reasons why other schools decide not to hire you," Mr. Bevel said, "but I want to thank you for providing this useful information to us. We will get back to you shortly with a conclusion of the investigation."

I thanked him and the Vice Provost for their time, and I went home. I felt pretty good sharing my experience with another person. I mean, it was nice I was able to get into some of the issues, and I hope this turns out for the best. After all, I was the one they took advantage of. I just did the job that I was tasked to do. Hell, I followed the instructed lesson in the way I was coached to provide it. So, I think the disability center, the lawyer, and the Vice Provost would take my side given the information that I shared with them.

When I got home, I pulled up to check the mail. I received a letter from The National Labor Relations Board. My complaint about Union mistreatment was summarily denied because the Teachers Union does not fall under the enforcement of the NLRB. They told me if I felt that I was wronged, I should try to file a complaint with another agency, but under the area informing of where and I needed to contact to file this complaint, the area was left blank.

Memory before the Arizona Teachers Academy

Before the Affordable Care Act/Obamacare, there was the CDC-INFO line. This 24-hour line, set up while President George W. Bush was in office, gave people with health concerns a national number of dispensing general health information so people could inform themselves without wasting time and money at the doctors. The first two tiers could be staffed by people with at least a high school diploma to save money by not paying for only healthcare professionals. Both Tier One and Tier Two read prepared health information strictly curated by the CDC and other appropriate Federal agencies. The prepared statements would attempt to answer all of the questions the public would ask. If we could not answer those questions with the prepared information or information from the website, we would offer to locate a healthcare provider in their area.

For the third tier, they represented medical professionals employed by another company, and they could provide more nuanced information primarily for medical professionals, health departments, hospitals, and other VIP individuals. Because they had medical training and familiarity with how to answer such questions, they could provide even more specialized knowledge than Tier One or Tier Two. However, they should not be confused with providing medical advice over the phone. It is nearly impossible to know what disease is causing illness by symptoms alone. A patient would need to be tested to identify, or eliminate, potential illnesses.

Working the third shift for a 24-hour information line, I often found extended periods of boredom. Sometimes, the calls would come once every hour. There was more than one time that I was awakened by the *ding* *ding* of an inbound call and a "hello?" I was often asleep during those times because the drudgery of the job bored me so damn much; however, the shift differential was very nice. The benefit of $16 an hour in 2006 was mostly offset by the complete isolation of working third shift. I would always arrive when the last group of workers from the second shift was leaving (or about to go), meaning we had nothing but our skeletal crew of two to three information specialists. We would also have the medical professional, a registered nurse, who could answer questions by healthcare professionals, and other higher-level staff. But it was mostly a ghost town.

Even though the company had multiple contracts with the United States government, the different areas were sequestered from the information line for the CDC due to the sensitive nature of the phone calls. The CDC-INFO line primary calls during the night and late-night hours almost always involved sexually transmitted diseases. HIV/AIDS was the primary topic for the majority of the calls whenever I would come into work. Overall, I think the primary subject matter of the third shift made the entire schedule very entertaining — when we did get calls. I mean, we had a little bit more leeway when it came to how we treated abusive callers or callers too lazy to go to the doctors. Considering that some people would rather call a random stranger than go to a doctor, I would occasionally show a bit of attitude towards people.

"Hello, thank you for calling 1-800-CDC-INFO. How can I help you?"

"I think I have a disease."

"If you have concerns about being exposed to a disease, the Centers for Disease Control and Prevention recommend that you get tested as soon as possible."

"But I am coughing, my nose will not stop running, and it sometimes burns when I pee."

"Okay..."

"Do you think I have AIDS?"

"Again, if you have concerns about being exposed to—"

"But do you think I have AIDS? The symptoms, are those AIDS symptoms?"

"As I said, if you are conc—"

"Just tell me if I have AIDS or not, 'kay?"

"Look! If you are concerned about being exposed to a disease, you need to get tested. For the life of me, it is physically impossible for me to diagnose you over the phone. Those symptoms…"

"Uh-huh."

"Those symptoms could be anything, anything. The only way you will know is for you to get tested."

"But—"

"No buts! If you are really concerned, you need to get tested. Just asking some random guy on the phone is like asking some random dude on the street. I don't know, and they sure as hell wouldn't know. So, if you are really concerned, do you want me to find a testing site in your area?"

As a reply to my question, the caller promptly hung up. I guess my truth bombs were a little too much for them to hear. I know it was scary for them, but what was I supposed to do? Lie to them? We weren't a counseling line, just an information line. I wasn't trained in that area, and I was definitely coached not to talk to callers like that in the future — no matter how rude they were.

But it was so fucking fun when I could get away with it.!

Either way, I provided a public service for those individuals who lacked the resources to go to an emergency room doctor, pay those outrageous fees, and didn't have the money to find a clinic in their area. So, even though I finished a number of advanced placement courses, even though my teachers felt sorry for me and gave me a $100 scholarship to go to college, a scholarship I never used, I rationalized my inability to attend college, handcuffed into an uneducated state because of poverty, by my work at a job that helped so many people in their time of need.

Rationalized was the correct statement because I do not know if I would have stayed another moment if given a chance to escape. But, unfortunately for me, my shackled leg needed to remain bound, tied to a position with no future unless I found a way to escape.

I wasted away in a third shift position for over five years before my chance. When it finally came for me to leave my prison of late-night solitude, I waited. I waited for months until I could get up the nerve to take a chance. When I finally did, when I finally had the nerve, the weight of those squandered minutes eased. I emailed my supervisor and his boss explaining that I needed to transition from this position, from this company, and return to school. I went into detail about how it will be too difficult for me to balance going to school during the day while also working at night. So, I thank them for their time and their opportunity.

Little did I know how leaving this job would drastically change my life forever…

February 27th, 2020

    With my normal mail delivery, I finally received responses from both the U.S. Department of Education, the Equal Employment Opportunity Commission. As I open each letter, I am hoping to hear some good news about the status of my complaints. The U.S. Government will help me out, especially since I didn't do anything wrong but complained about how my rights were being harmed. I know both *The University* and *The School District* are both taking advantage of me with their sham investigations because I just assert my rights.

    After opening the first letter, I was shocked to read horrible news. In the case of the U.S. Department of Education, I was notified that neither *The School District* nor *The University* violated my Civil Rights by delaying my graduation by six months. The letter went on further to state in a roundabout way *The School District* and *The University* are legally allowed to transmit my personal information to any and all parties that have an educational interest. So, in other words, even though the information was laughably untrue and harmful for my future employment prospects, neither party can really be harmed by the dissemination of the information, especially if it is behind closed doors.

    The School District does not have to fear State or Federal laws regarding punishment for retaliatory actions because I have to prove they did something wrong with the intent harmed me. It always boils down to my word against the teachers and their fellow union members. Unfortunately for me, no matter what I say or do, they are legally allowed to transmit as long as it relates to education. Since I cannot prove what they say behind closed doors, Mr. Saille, Mr.

Sona, and Mr. Cichy effectively ending my teaching career before it even begins.

For my complaint to the EEOC, I was told that my concern did not count as a Civil Rights violation because, according to the records provided by the other party, there was not a clear violation of laws enforced by the EEOC. In addition, the lawyer from *The School District* provided statements from multiple employees (many of whom were not there) corroborating all of Mr. Cichy's claims of me acting inappropriately. The federal agency further explained if I have any concerns about any specific laws that violate my personal privacy, I could file a complaint with the U.S. Department of Education about what I may feel is a FERPA violation. After reading all the information, I realized the letters basically told me the Federal government did not have my back. So, I opened a letter from *The University* and the Office of the Vice Provost.

While I was sitting there, about to cry uncontrollably for only the second time in my life, my phone dings, notifying me that I received an email.

The email, the stab to my barely beating heart, was from *The University*. According to Dr. Indea, she denied any wrongdoing had occurred. Every policy was followed to the letter, "*The University* gave you additional time to complete the student teaching assignment because of your health history allowing you to have extra time. Because of your health history, we are going to overlook new information that we discovered during our investigation," and she shared lies by Mr. Sona, Mr. Cichy, and Mr. Saille. They even lied and said I was physically violent with a student. Of course, if I was ever violent with a student, I would have been expelled from the Teachers Program, if not expelled from *The University* entirely. But because I spoke up, and Mr. Cichy decided to just make shit up, she went wild. Hell, Captain Fuckface likely tasked his students to make their responses nothing more than a creative writing assignment (I guess writing the wrong dates wasn't a big enough giveaway — or *The University* was never looking for truth, just an excuse).

I honestly believe they were trying to silence me and retaliate against me as a prevention mechanism. Even their statement of never wanting to host other students again seems pretty fishy and pretty much unneeded. Why was the question asked by *The University*? Why did these teachers even volunteer this information? Don't we have a teacher shortage right now? Why would they want to end my career? Did I unearth something, or did they just not like me because I wouldn't remain silent? I mean, why even interject they would not want to have other student teachers in the future? Why would they do such a thing to someone who only wants to help? A person who is trying to pull themselves up by their bootstraps? Is it because I pissed off the wrong person? It seems like they were just making up stuff to cover their own asses for being bad mentors, maybe even bigots, and I speak out against their blind spots, and I am the bad guy because I took a stand..

WHAT THE FUCK?!?!!!

This was the opportunity for *The University* to make everything alright, make everything whole. Still, I have a sneaking suspicion that I was sacrificed to promote their own business interests with *The School District* instead of taking a stand against real oppression and egregious misconduct. If I was a pretty person, if I was a younger person, if I was something more desirable (not just a walking, talking extension of the State's wallet), *The University* may have done something to help and protect one of their students instead of leaving me to the wolves, leaving me to potentially pay back the entire $20,000 grant as unsubsidized loan. How the hell am I going to afford an unsubsidized loan? Those teachers and *The University* want to rob my family, my children, of an opportunity for them to have a bright future. If they really cared about future generations, *The University* would have sided with me, protected me. Instead, because of their apathy, ignoring my plaintive cries, I am in a position where my own children will have to re-live the same horrible situation that I grew up experiencing.

I remember when Mr. Saille and Mr. Sona told me to **not complain**, to not switch out of her classroom — much less switch out to another High School entirely. They wanted me to come in with a fake smile plastered across my face like I got away with doing something wrong,

NO!

I could not just continue to show up to that school.

I could not continue to look in the eyes of some bigot.

I could not be in the presence of their flowing toxicity, an unstitched wound seeping hostility's pus all over me, their students, and anyone who really wants to make a difference.

I knew I should have switched away from Mr. Saille. I knew I should have been distraught when I was written up before my third observation. I was too trusting of Mr. Saille or *The School District* really wanting more teachers. I should have instantly questioned when the Teacher Program manager at *The University* told me how there would be an extra observer who would accompany Mr. Saille to make sure I was scored appropriately. I was "given" the option to request my own observer from the teaching program, but my cohort's favorite professor Dr. Smith turned down both chances to observe me. She was busy both times, and she saw me mock teach in class multiple times before I even began interning. So, I was wronged, and I don't even have a teaching job right now for next Fall Semester.

So, I guess…I guess Arizona wasted money on my education because some teachers would rather promote their talking point about there being a teacher shortage, a political tool to gain more money from taxpayers, instead of working with a brain injury survivor, a brain injury survivor who pulled themselves up from the gravel, the dirt, the injury and strived to make the next generation better than the one before it.

I really felt like I wasted almost two years of my life without anything to show for it. I guess the districts will try to keep me as a substitute, so they will not have to pay me a fair wage, provide me benefits, or even be treated like a person who has a Masters of Education, a Bachelor of Arts in English, a Bachelor of Arts in Communication, graduated Summa Cum Laude, was a member of Amnesty International (even saw Joan Baez at the 50th Anniversary of Amnesty International Conference in San Francisco California), or anything other colorful adventure I experienced to help future students.

All of this was meaningless because I didn't keep my mouth shut. I didn't let them mistreat me, belittle me, shame me without saying a word. I had to pick myself up from the dirt, and I spoke up against accepting their unearned maltreatment because I was just a new teacher. Even with a scrapped shoulder. A bleeding cheek. I still picked myself up from the rocks that marred my flesh. I stood when the doctors told me that I should stay down, lay down, stay home and collect disability benefits.

NO!

My mother was forced to do that because an illness took hold of her, never letting go until her death. I will put my family through that same problem. To paraphrase Cyrano de Bergerac, I will fight, and fight, and continue fighting until the last ember of energy leaves these limbs. These sacred cows are my proverbial log. My piece of wretched, corrupted timber, trying to cause me to collapse in my partner's arms and fade away. So, I honestly believe this from the bottom of my heart, Mr. Sona, Mr. Cichy, and

Mr. Saille, if you were not happy with your own life, you wouldn't have felt the need to disrupt mine just because you made poor life choices. Money is not the reason some of us want to be teachers.

The next time they want to march on the State Capitol, I suggest they march to become better people — not just line their own pockets with gold. If teachers like them really care, if they really want to show an effort to promote a better generation of citizens, their students will be the better for it. Unfortunately, until they decide to make those required changes, I believe nothing will really improve. Arizona Education will be stuck in neutral. Everything will boil down to the same problems, same teachers complaining about how they need more help, their classes are too large, parents are not helping out enough, and their students will suffer from their hubris and their endless complaining.

Memory before the Arizona Teachers Academy

I moved into my first house that I have ever owned. It was actually a few blocks away from where I cast my ballot in the last election. I think it was pretty much fate the property was available, and I moved to this lonely, foreclosed house with a splendid nature preserve behind me. The house stood as a monument to not living in a ratty apartment any longer. This monument was a testament that I would not have to worry about loud neighbors fighting over the last crust of bread or neighbors who played their damn music way too loud.

For my best guess, these were all track homes. Because the developers for the community wanted to get the NIMBY ("not in my back yard") crowd, every house looked exactly the same. There was no variation in the color, features, or anything that would cause them to be drastically different from one another. It was a copied and pasted home. But since my history was filled with living in apartment complexes or rundown hotels for most of my life, it was a nice change of scenery.

Even with every house on my block looking exactly the same, the developer took it one step further by establishing a Home Owners Association. Under the tyranny of the HOA, they would issue warnings and then fines. If there were any weeds in the yard, a warning followed by a fine. If your house was painted the wrong color, fine and request to change it back. Anyone who deviated from the prescribed appearance of the neighborhood would receive a bill for their insolence.

But as a new stage of my life, I can gladly say that I picked a wonderful place to live. The neighbors were very quiet, never having very loud parties or anything of the sort. Hell, I don't think I have seen any of them, only their parked cars. So, this was utterly different from all my prior experiences. Also, I did not live in a place owned by someone else. This one would be all mine.

Now, I know that I didn't have any furniture, and I slept in the guest room because this was the only room that had curtains in front of the windows, but I was still overjoyed to have it. When I looked out of the window, right in front of where I sleep, there was a tall saguaro who wished me a warm hello (a warm welcome to the possibilities of what the day would bring).

There was only one negative.

Since the house was built on a side street off the beaten path, maybe a bit too far from civilization, definitely far away from the bus route that could take me to work. I had to trek for over a mile to catch a bus. This meant that I needed to time my departures perfectly. If I left too early, I would be sitting at the bus stop and waiting. If I left too late, I would arrive to see the bus as it pulled away.

This bus took me to Metrocenter Mall, a place in the twilight of its former glory. The mall was near my first apartment after I moved in to be closer to the woman I was seeing at the time. It was a small studio apartment, but it was the first time I ever lived on my own without any roommates. I could afford it with my hourly wage as a shift manager for a burger restaurant off of I-17 and Thunderbird.

Either way, form my current house and after walking to the bus stop, I would take the bus that did a straight line down 35th Avenue. After the bus deposited me at the mall, I transferred over to the Route 90 bus and traveled down Dunlap Ave., and I was deposited right in front of the Art Institute of Phoenix and Argosy University. It wasn't perfect, but I knew it was better than the alternative. I didn't want to make a 20-mile roundtrip on foot (or even on a bike). If I did that, tired would not explain the level of fatigue I felt every workday.

But as I look back on what happened and what could have been, I think I should have left at five in the evening more often. When I left at five o'clock to catch the bus, I always walked by this empty field next to the Loop 101 access road. My reward for the early departure was the reflection of day's dying embers upon the grey and brown rocks, the collection of weeds, wild shrubs, and that one solemn Palo Verde tree who dug for any ounce of water it could find in that parched, arid earth.

It was a sight to behold.

Every time I inched closer to the bus stop during this calm and relaxed moment, and the perfect image engraved itself within my soul. The image bloomed within my psyche and calmed any frayed nerves. I mumbled to myself everything was okay. Everything was tranquil. Everything was the way it should be. Everything would remain this way because fortune allowed it to happen.

The hawk who circled the neighborhood, a hawk who controlled the pigeon population, made tight loops above my head. It looked for its next meal. I just marveled at how nature could be so pristine, so perfect, when it could be so violent. And I should be happy to be alive to experience it as dust picked up by the tireless wind, swirled end over end across the field, across the sidewalk, across the street. The well-traveled dust stopped to pay a new mound of thirty, sun-parched dried-out clay a visit.

As the bus I rode on pulled away, as the scene disappeared from my view, I knew what all of this represented: tranquility. Tranquility feeding into itself, lopping over round and round. An imperfect infinite dream. Like everything else — in time.

ABOUT THE AUTHOR

David Redkey, awarded the Arizona Teachers Academy scholarship in 2018, is a former teacher who writes about experiences of those who may be labeled less than by others. He's a graduate from Glendale Community College and Arizona State University. David lives in Arizona with his family while also trying to make each day better than the last.

ABOUT THE PUBLISHER

TBI Writer, LLC — founded by a traumatic brain injury survivor — aims to publish quality, thought-provoking pieces by any creator who decides to share their life experiences or products of their own imagination. Our endeavors promotes a more encouraging, inclusive environment for whoever wishes to share these viewpoints of the world. Because through understanding and acceptance, we can move forward together.

Made in the USA
Las Vegas, NV
26 November 2021

35339483R00154